SEEKIN

Riches

The Book of Hebrews

MW00615969

SEEKING GOD'S GREAT
Riches

The Book of Hebrews

DOROTHY DAVIS

REGULAR BAPTIST
RBP **Press**

Dedication

To Dawn and Michael,
who are running their race with patience
as they look unto Jesus

Seeking God's Great Riches: The Book of Hebrews

© 2004 Regular Baptist Press • Arlington Heights, Illinois

www.RegularBaptistPress.org • 1-800-727-4440

RBP5316 • ISBN: 978-1-59402-154-1

All rights reserved. Printed in U.S.A.

Third Printing: 2016

All rights reserved. Except as permitted under U.S. Copyright Law, no part of this publication may be reproduced, distributed, or transmitted in any form or by any means, or stored in a database or retrieval system, without the prior written permission of the publisher.

Contents

Preface

Looking for something? Perhaps you've been searching for a lost piece of jewelry, a recipe you cut from a magazine, or that elusive sock that is hiding from its twin! We seem to spend much time *seeking* in this life. Some of our efforts are rewarded; some are futile.

Human beings, whom God has created with spirit, soul, and body, have a spiritual longing that they seek to satisfy. In our world today hundreds of pathways promise to lead seekers to spiritual peace and prosperity, but often they lead to emptiness, doubt, and at worst, enslavement. Only one way leads to a real relationship with God, to spiritual fulfillment and assured eternal life. Jesus Christ declared, "I am the way, the truth, and the life: no man cometh unto the Father, but by me" (John 14:6).

The New Testament book of Hebrews presents the absolute superiority of Jesus Christ and the true Christian faith that embraces Him. We are urged to seek Him and the glorious promises of our God, Who abides with us as we journey through life.

Let us, then, seek after the spiritual treasures that come from God's vast storehouse of riches. They are found only in Him Who is the greatest of all God's riches: Jesus Christ, our Lord!

Introduction

The Lord Jesus told a parable in which people "receive the word with joy; and these have no root, which for a while believe, and in time of temptation fall away" (Luke 8:13). The recipients of the letter to the Hebrews were facing persecution for following Christ. Some were being tempted to "fall away," to go back into Judaism (the keeping of the Old Testament laws) to avoid persecution. Some of these people, perhaps, were not even truly Christians because they had never received Christ as Savior by faith alone. To come so close to the truth, and to purposely reject Christ, put them in great spiritual danger.

To these people the letter of Hebrews was written. Who wrote it? That fact is still a mystery. Some think it was the apostle Paul, based on similarities between his epistles and Hebrews. Others think it was someone else who was a respected church leader, but not one of the apostles who had seen Christ (Hebrews 2:3). "The writer" (as I will refer to him) was eloquent, well-versed in the Old Testament Scriptures, with which the book of Hebrews is saturated. He presented—almost as a lawyer would—a very strong, well laid-out case for the excellency of the new covenant of grace that came by Jesus Christ, God's own Son. Why should these people go back to Judaism when God has given a way far superior?

Seek a life of grace, a life of faith. Seek the Lord Jesus Christ. This is the persuasive argument of the book of Hebrews.

How to Use This Study

Each lesson in this study is divided into five sections. Follow these suggestions as you prepare each lesson.

I. LOOK INTO YOUR HEART

Following the introductory comments, these questions will prepare your heart to study God's Word. These questions will not be discussed in class.

II. SEARCH THE SCRIPTURES

The questions in this section concentrate on the actual text of God's Word and will help you understand what God's Word says.

III. DISCOVER THE TRUTH

As you answer the questions in this section, you will see how the truths of God's Word apply to your life.

IV. CLAIM YOUR TREASURE

This section is personal. It is designed as a starting point to help you put God's truth into practice.

V. REJOICE IN YOUR RICHES

These final words will help seal firmly in your mind what you learned from the Bible passage.

Seek the Son

Hebrews 1 and 2

"But we see Jesus, who was made a little lower than the angels for the suffering of death, crowned with glory and honour; that he by the grace of God should taste death for every man" (Hebrews 2:9).

Just a glimpse! Have you ever endured being squeezed by a crowd just to catch a glimpse of some famous person? Perhaps it was a president, a sports hero, or some celebrity. If only you could see that person in real life, just for a moment!

Remember Zacchaeus? In Luke 19 we are told that the diminutive tax collector couldn't see the One Who was coming to his town; the crowd was too great. So he humbled himself, climbed a tree, and waited for a glimpse of this One about Whom wondrous things were told. Zacchaeus was not disappointed, for he received much more than a glimpse. Jesus Christ paid Zacchaeus personal attention, and his life was never the same.

Seek the Son. You are not just one of the crowd to Him. He cares personally for you. Once you know Him, your life will never be the same.

I. LOOK INTO YOUR HEART

What role does Jesus play in your life?

____ I don't know much about Him.

____ I know a little about Him.

____ I know Him; He is my Savior and Lord.

II. SEARCH THE SCRIPTURES

Read Hebrews 1 and 2.

1. In Hebrews 1:1–4 we are introduced to the Lord Jesus Christ. According to these verses, what is one reason God sent His Son to earth?

2. From verses 2–4, list some of the truths you learn about Jesus Christ.

3. Read verses 5–9 and give three reasons why Christ is superior to the angels.

4. Finish the chapter by reading verses 8–14 as a unit. To Whom is Jesus, the Son, equated in verses 8 and 10?

5. What work is attributed to Christ in verse 10?

6. What qualities (attributes) of Christ are mentioned in verse 12?

7. What promise did the Father make to the Son, as mentioned in verse 13? Read Psalm 110.

8. What is the job of angels according to verse 14?

9. Read Hebrews 2:1–4. Verse 1 begins with the word "therefore." The writer was connecting all he had just said with all he was about to say. What warning did he give in verse 1? How is this related to chapter 1?

10. (a) "The things which we have heard" in verse 1 is equated with what word in Hebrews 2:3?

(b) What are we told NOT to do?

11. (a) Where did this idea of "salvation" come from (v. 3)?

(b) How do we know these things are true (v. 4)?

12. In Hebrews 2:5–8 we see the position of man in God's plan for the universe. What is man's "job description" as set forth here?

13. Hebrews 1 presents the Lord Jesus as God, stressing His deity. In Hebrews 2: 9–18 the writer discussed Christ's humanity: Jesus Christ is both fully God and fully man. As God, taking on a human body, He came to earth to dwell among us. In doing so, what was Jesus willing to do (v. 9; see also Philippians 2:5–8)?

14. Why did Jesus come to earth and die on a cross? Read the following verses to formulate your answer: Romans 3:8, 9, 23; 1 Corinthians 15:3, 4; 1 Peter 2:24.

15. The Word of God declares that forgiveness of sins and eternal life (salvation) are a gift. How does a person receive this gift? See John 1:12, 3:16, and Ephesians 2:8 and 9.

16. What are some of the results accomplished for us by Christ's incarnation and sacrificial death, as stated in these verses in Hebrews 2?

Verse 9

Verse 10

Verses 11–13

Verse 14

Verse 15

Verses 16, 17

Verse 18

III. DISCOVER THE TRUTH

We have had a glimpse of the Lord Jesus Christ in Hebrews 1 and 2. As God, He stooped to become a man and enter the stage of human history so that He could speak to us of the Father (1:2). He tasted death for every person by dying for each one's sins on the cross (2:9), and as a result, He destroyed the power of death and the Devil. Furthermore, He became our merciful and faithful brother, willing and able to help us in all our spiritual need. Many people today (even though they say they read the Bible) claim that Jesus was just a prophet or a teacher.

1. Write down five facts from Hebrews 1 and 2 that prove that Jesus is more than a prophet or teacher.

2. Angels are popular beings today, seemingly society's generic mode of acknowledging God. Biblically, who are angels according to Hebrews 1:7 and 14? Why are they not to be worshiped?

3. People also exalt creation in our day. Why must we not worship creation (Hebrews 1:10–12; Romans 1:25)? Why should we treat creation with respect?

4. Hebrews 1 teaches us that Jesus Christ—God the Son, Creator, Sustainer, and King—came to this earth. Chapter 2 declares that His mission was to suffer and die as a representative of man, making reconciliation for our sins and defeating death and Satan. The writer warned in 2:3 that we must not neglect the great salvation God offers to us. In what ways do unbelieving people neglect their souls' eternal destiny? (See, for example, Luke 12:16–21.)

5. Do believing Christians neglect their salvation? How do they do this? Read 2 Peter 1:5–9.

IV. CLAIM YOUR TREASURE

God has great riches for you in Christ! What decision do you need to make as a result of your study in His Word? Select one of the following decisions and spend some moments in prayer, asking the Lord to work in your life as you seek Him and His excellent riches through Christ.

____ I have never before understood that Jesus Christ is God, dying on the cross to pay the penalty for my sin. I want to put my faith in Him right now, inviting Him into my life and receiving His gift of forgiveness and salvation.

____ I have not been giving Jesus Christ the worship and honor of my heart for which He is worthy. I have neglected my salvation, and I want to renew my commitment to my Lord right now.

V. REJOICE IN YOUR RICHES

Now that you have seen Jesus, the true Jesus, is not your heart filled with wonder and worship? He is far above the created beings, "far above all principality, and power, and might, and dominion, and every name that is named, not only in this world, but also in that which is to come" (Ephesians 1:21). Jesus Christ is God's greatest treasure. If there is someone or something to seek, it is the Lord Jesus. Let us begin there. He became a man to bear human sin and put Himself under God's wrath. He shared our sufferings so He could sympathize with us. He defeated sin, death, and Satan so He could free us.

Have you received Him? Is He the Savior of your life?

Seek and Enter His Rest

Hebrews 3 and 4

"For he that is entered into his rest, he also hath ceased from his own works, as God did from his" (Hebrews 4:10).

A weary band of men, women, and children stepped out on the shores of a strange and wild land, later to be called Massachusetts. Long and perilous had been their journey to this place of freedom and hope. They had sought for a refuge and a new beginning, and now they were to enter it and make it their own. Many trials lay ahead, but by diligent labor and supreme sacrifice, the Pilgrims would find a haven where they could worship God in truth and serve Him unfettered. For the spent travelers, a place of rest was at hand.

As Christians, we are pilgrims in this life, seeking a land of spiritual peace, promise, and rest. The land is open before us. Let us step out in faith to the shores of God's land. Here He will give us rest, His rest.

I. LOOK INTO YOUR HEART

Are you emotionally or mentally weary right now?
For what are you failing to trust God at present?

II. SEARCH THE SCRIPTURES

Read Hebrews 3 and 4.

1. Read Hebrews 2:17—3:6. Jesus Christ became a human being. According to verse 18, how was His earthly life like ours?

2. The quality of Christ focused on in this section (2:17—3:16) is His faithfulness. (a) In what ways was Christ faithful?

(b) Why is it important that Christ was faithful?

3. We are instructed in Hebrews 3:1 to consider Christ. How does His faithfulness affect us according to verse 6?

The Scriptures remind us that the Lord is our shepherd and we are His sheep (Psalm 95:7). God wants to lead us through the wilderness to a land of still waters and green pastures, but often we are wayward and stubborn, seeking our own way (Isaiah 53:6).

4. Read Hebrews 3:7–11, which quotes Psalm 95:7–11. God wants us to be faithful, but what is sometimes our response to God's leading, as pointed out in these verses?

5. Unbelief is a sin that, in its vast ramifications, stands side by side with pride. Unbelief fails to take into account the living God, which is of great offense to Him. Read the following verses and explain why God rebuked the person mentioned.

Numbers 20:7–12

John 20:24–27

6. What is unbelief called in Hebrews 3:12? How is it described?

7. What are believers told to do in 3:13? What does this mean?

8. Read Hebrews 3:14—4:2. The writer used the wilderness-wandering Israelites to warn us about unbelief. (a) Of what were the Israelites guilty according to the writer of Hebrews?

(b) Of what must *we* be careful according to 4:1?

What is this "rest" that God has for us? The "rest" of salvation is ours when we stop working to earn God's forgiveness and receive by faith the eternal life Christ offers (Matthew 11:28). Then there is the "rest" of sanctification (Christian living). We go on to learn that we live daily by faith in Christ's power at work in us. It is resting in our union with Christ (Romans 6:4, 5; Galatians 2:20; Colossians 3:3, 4).

9. Read Hebrews 4:3–11. As stated in these verses, what is the greatest obstacle we face to entering into a state of spiritual rest (living by faith in Christ's power)? In what verses is this obstacle mentioned?

10. Read Hebrews 4:11–16. When unbelief grips our hearts, we slip into the self-effort mode: I must change myself; I must try harder not to sin; etc. Since self-effort is the work of the flesh, we will always fail (Romans 7:18). Only the power of the Holy Spirit at work within us will produce holiness. Now read again Hebrews 4:11. "Aha," you may say. " 'Let us labour'; so we do have to work!" Look up the following verses and jot down what our spiritual labor is to be.

John 15:4, 5

Romans 12:1, 2

Romans 13:14

Colossians 3:1, 2

James 4:7, 8

11. Hebrews 4:11 warns about unbelief. How will our deepest spiritual struggles be exposed, as expressed in verses 12 and 13?

12. How is the Word of God described in verse 12? What does it judge?

13. Verse 16 instructs us about our unbelief. Where are we to go? How do we go there? Who is there?

14. What is our High Priest like? What will He do for us (4:14–16)?

15. (a) Since we have a High Priest, the Word of God, and the throne of grace, what should we do (v. 14)?

(b) What does this verse mean to you?

III. DISCOVER THE TRUTH

1. Hebrews 3 and 4 remind us of Christ's faithfulness. We, in turn, are urged to be faithful to the end. In fact, we are told to fear falling away from God (4:1). (a) What persons can you think of in the Scriptures who began well but fell away from God due to unbelief?

(b) What warnings should we take from these examples? Read 2 Corinthians 13:5, 1 John 2:19, and 2 Peter 1:10–12.

2. A believer who is living by faith will have inward rest and peace. How do symptoms of unbelief show in the following areas?
Thoughts/attitudes

Words

Actions

As a rule, falling away from God rarely happens overnight in a believer's life. It is a backward trend that occurs by a series of wrong choices and a progressive neglect of the spiritual basics: considering God's Word, open and honest prayer, fellowship with godly believers. As these basics are neglected, one's heart begins to harden. Yet we may deny that we are regressing spiritually due to sin's deceitfulness (3:13).

3. How is each of the following elements a vital ingredient in renewing and maintaining a relationship with the living God?

Bible reading/meditation

Prayer

Regular church attendance

4. As believers, how can we carry out our responsibility to exhort one another daily?

5. There are four "let us" commands in chapter 4: let us fear lest we fall short (v. 1); let us labor to enter His rest (v. 11); let us hold fast our profession of faith (v. 14); let us come boldly to the throne of grace (v. 16). In which area(s) are you doing fairly well? Which command(s) do you find most challenging? What changes do you need to make?

IV. CLAIM YOUR TREASURE

Has the Lord spoken to you through His Word? What decision do you need to make as a result of your study? Select one of the following responses and spend some moments in prayer, asking the Lord to work in your heart in that area of need.

____ I have not been faithful to the Lord. I want to fully surrender my life to Him today and begin to seek Him daily.

____ I have been struggling with unbelief about _____. I am asking the Lord for faith so that I can have rest and peace as I look to Him to work in this matter.

____ I have been neglecting time in the Bible, times of open, honest prayer, and/or regular church attendance. I am looking to the Lord to work in my heart as I commit myself to a plan of personal growth.

V. REJOICE IN YOUR RICHES

Just as the Mayflower carried the Pilgrims to their land of rest and promise, so Christ is our vessel of power to spiritual living. Our daily responsibility is to keep ourselves "in Him" by reading His Word and allowing it to convict and change us as the Spirit works in our hearts. And we must pray, coming boldly to the God of all grace and mercy, Who alone can empower us in every need and situation. As we keep ourselves by faith in Christ, sin will diminish and spiritual rest will fill our hearts. What joy and peace He can give when we look to Him in faith! Have you experienced the richness of resting in Christ?

L E S S O N 3

Seeking Higher Ground

Hebrews 5 and 6

"That ye be not slothful, but followers of them who through faith and patience inherit the promises" (Hebrews 6:12).

Recently I listened to an interview with a baseball player who was having a great major league career. The interviewer asked if there was anything further to learn or to strive for. Resolutely, the athlete explained that he must always keep progressing, expecting more from himself, or he would become apathetic and his career would plummet downhill.

How much more, as believers, must we always push on to new plateaus, progressing in both our knowledge of Scripture and our service to God? A well-known hymn makes this request: "Lord, plant my feet on higher ground." In addition to unbelief, we must continually fight off smugness, apathy, and mental laziness if we are to obtain the full commendation of Christ.

Clear out the cobwebs. Put on your marching boots. We're breaking camp and moving on because today—right now—we must seek higher ground.

I. LOOK INTO YOUR HEART

1. How would you rate your present determination to learn new truths from Scripture?

poor   fair   good   very good

2. How would you rate your present participation in service to the Lord?

not enough   just right   over-committed

II. SEARCH THE SCRIPTURES

Read Hebrews 5 and 6.

1. In chapter 5 the writer of Hebrews continued his meditation on our Great High Priest, Jesus Christ. What was the job of the high priest in the Old Testament, as mentioned in Hebrews 5:1–4?

2. Read Hebrews 5:5–10. Verses 7 and 8 refer to Jesus' time of prayer in the Garden of Gethsemane before His crucifixion. (See Matthew 26:36–39.) (a) According to Hebrews 5:7, was Christ's prayer heard?

(b) How did the Father answer?

(c) What was Christ's response to God's will?

3. The Greek words for Hebrews 5:8 state, "He learned from the things which He suffered." As a man, Christ learned about the human aspect of a relationship with the Father as He experienced life on earth. What might Jesus have "learned" as He went through His trials, crucifixion, and resurrection?

4. Read Hebrews 5:11–14. No doubt you've heard the expression, "Stop being a baby!" In effect the writer of Hebrews was saying that to the recipients of his letter. According to verse 11, what was their problem? What might this description mean?

5. Evidently those people had been believers for a time and should have been entering a state of spiritual maturity ("ought to be teachers," v. 12). (a) What object lesson did the writer use in Hebrews 5:12–14 to describe their condition?

(b) At what point in their development were those Hebrew Christians?

6. Reread Hebrews 5:12–14 carefully. How, then, are we to progress past the "milk" stage as believers?

7. Read Hebrews 6:1–9. As one in a leadership position, the writer stated his expectations for believers. (a) What must be the goal of every believer according to Hebrews 6:1?

(b) How is this accomplished (vv. 1, 2)?

Admittedly, Hebrews 6:4–8 is a difficult passage to understand. The verses seem to say that a person who falls away from the Lord will lose her salvation. But we must consider the context. Remember, the writer had just urged those believers to *progress*. What happens if believers *regress*? They put themselves in danger of falling into error, forsaking Christ, and not repenting. Continuing apart from Christ, they would publicly shame Him and perhaps be committing "sin unto death," a spiritual state so far removed from the Lord that He prematurely ends a believer's life (1 John 5:16).

8. (a) How does the Lord view such totally backslidden believers (v. 8)?

(b) What will be the outcome for such people as indicated by verse 8? (See also 1 Corinthians 3:13–15 and John 15:6.)

9. In Hebrews 6:9–12 the writer encouraged his readers even though he had just rebuked (5:11–14) and warned (6:4–8) them. For what qualities did he commend them (6:10)?

10. (a) What qualities did he urge the believers to possess that would have spiritually moved them to higher ground (Hebrews 6:11, 12)?

(b) What were they not to be?

11. Abraham, the great Old Testament saint, is used as an example of the believer who pushed on to higher ground because he trusted the faithfulness of God. Answer the following questions based on Hebrews 6:13–17. (a) What promise did God make to Abraham (vv. 13, 14)?

(b) What was Abraham's response to God's promises (v. 15)?

(c) What was the result in Abraham's life (v. 15)?

(d) Why did God swear by Himself when He made His promise (vv. 13, 16, 17)?

In order to forge ahead, to progress toward a goal, people need motivation. They expect some good to come from their perseverance. For the Christian, that motivation is hope. Hope is the expectation of faith's fulfillment: all for which we are trusting God will come to pass. According to Hebrews 6:18 and 19, our hope rests in two things: God's oath, based on His name and character, and God's promises, based on the certainty of His Word.

12. Look up the following verses and summarize their truths about God's promises and character.

Numbers 23:19

Nehemiah 9:7, 8

Romans 4:20, 21

13. How does our hope in God's promises and character affect our lives (Hebrews 6:18, 19)?

14. Hebrews 6 ends by again drawing our attention to Jesus. Without Him we have no hope. His presence at the Father's right hand as our intercessor assures us of eternal life and eternal acceptance with God. Every promise from God comes back to Jesus. How does 2 Corinthians 1:18–20 confirm this? What do these verses mean?

III. DISCOVER THE TRUTH

1. How, then, do Christians progress to higher ground? First of all, like Christ in the Garden of Gethsemane, we must be fully submitted to the Father's will for our lives, totally surrendered. (a) What causes people to fear and hold back control of their lives from God's hand?

(b) How can these fears be removed?

2. Various Biblical passages assert that we learn through suffering. (See, for instance, Psalm 119:67; 1 Peter 4:1, 2; James 1:3, 4.) (a) What are some of the things you have learned through times of suffering in your life?

(b) What may hinder our learning during these times?

3. Why might believers today remain at an immature spiritual level? Is it due to a lack of intelligence, or is there some other cause? Jot down your ideas. (Refer to Luke 8:4–15 as well.)

4. God redeemed us, but He left us on earth to minister to both the saved and the unsaved. We are to be witnesses to unbelievers (Acts 1:8) and encouragers to our fellow believers (Hebrews 3:13; 10:24, 25). What benefits do you find in being involved in a ministry to other believers?

5. What are some wrong motives for being involved in ministry?

6. What are proper motivations for ministry? (Refer to Hebrews 6:10 and other Scriptures you know.)

Christians often become over-committed in ministry. Because they feel they can't say no, they take on too many obligations and end up discouraged or defeated or both. They may mistakenly equate busyness with spirituality: the more I do for Christ, the more spiritual I am. But God wants us *to be* first, then *to do*.

7. How can you determine when to commit to a ministry and when to say no?

8. Our motivation for growth and service is Jesus, our Lord. We will see Him again, and we want to please Him. The writer of Hebrews used such words as "diligence," "endurance," and "hope." What keeps you pressing on to higher ground in your walk with the Lord? What do you do when you hit a low?

IV. CLAIM YOUR TREASURE

Has the Lord spoken to you through His Word? What decision do you need to make as a result of your study? Select one of the following decisions and spend some moments in prayer, asking the Lord to work in your heart as you seek Him.

_____ I need to fully surrender my life to God's control. Like Christ, I want to do the Father's will as He shows it to me.

_____ I am going through some hard times right now, but I want to learn the lessons God has for me as I go through them.

_____ I have been mentally lazy about reading and learning God's Word. In order to grow, I am committing myself to spend time in God's Word daily.

_____ I sense that I have been regressing spiritually. I need to repent of my sin of _____ (be specific). I want to seek the Lord anew and be diligent about following Him.

_____ I have not been serving the Lord in ministry to others. I will seek His will and ask Him to direct me to the work He has for me to do.

____ I am burned out or too busy in ministry. I am neglecting my spiritual life (spending too little time in reading God's Word and prayer) and my other responsibilities. I am going to renew fellowship with God and spend time in prayer, revaluating my commitments and determining which ministries are God's will for me.

V. REJOICE IN YOUR RICHES

The apostle Paul said, "Not as though I had already attained, either were already perfect: but I follow after, if that I may apprehend that for which also I am apprehended of Christ Jesus" (Philippians 3:12). It has been said that in our Christian lives we never stand still; we are either going forward or backward. We must always push on, learning through trials, discovering new truths in the Word, seeing God work in the lives of others through our labor of love for Him. As we set our minds above, where Christ is seated in the heavenlies (Colossians 3:1, 2), we will move on, in hope, to higher levels of faith.

A Relationship, Not a Religion

Hebrews 7 and 8

"Wherefore he is able also to save them to the uttermost that come unto God by him, seeing he ever liveth to make intercession for them" (Hebrews 7:25).

Why would a person spend years searching for a long-lost parent, brother, or sister? To gratify personal curiosity? Discover family medical information? These reasons are sometimes given. But most often the driving force behind such a search is the desire for a relationship that will satisfy the soul of the seeker. "I want to *know* my loved one," the person would probably say.

After the great Flood of Noah's day, mankind chose to not "retain God in their knowledge" (Romans 1:28). They forsook their Creator and worshiped other things. Yet, man still had a God-given capacity for worship and an inner longing for a relationship with his Maker.

Religion is man's effort to reach God. But only God can establish a relationship with us, a relationship we desire and need. Jesus Christ, the only Mediator between God and man, has enabled us to know God and please Him. Are you practicing a religion or enjoying a relationship?

I. LOOK INTO YOUR HEART

Which of the following choices will make you acceptable to God? Put a check beside your answer.

____ 1. Giving money to the church

____ 2. Keeping the Ten Commandments

____ 3. Confessing sins to a priest

____ 4. Praying through a mediator other than Jesus Christ

____ 5. Becoming a child of God by receiving through faith Christ's
death and resurrection to forgive your sins

II. SEARCH THE SCRIPTURES

Read Hebrews 7 and 8.

1. Melchizedek has been mentioned already in the book of Hebrews
(5:6, 10; 6:20). In Hebrews 7 he is presented in-depth as a "type," or
picture, of Christ. From Hebrews 7:1–3, list the ways in which this Old
Testament priest reminds us of Jesus Christ. (Read Genesis 14:13–20 as
the background for this Hebrews passage.)

2. What was Abraham's response to this great priest and king (Hebrews 7:2, 4)?

In Hebrews 7:5–10 the writer laid the groundwork to prove to the
early Jewish believers that faith in Christ is far superior to the levitical
priesthood of the Old Testament system. Under those religious laws, the
priests could only be from the tribe of Levi. Yet Abraham, the great father
of the Jewish nation, and symbolically his descendants (which included
the Levites), paid tithes and tribute to another priest acknowledged by
God, Melchizedek.

3. According to Hebrews 7:6 and 7, what did Abraham receive from this priest?

4. Read Psalm 110, a "messianic" psalm. (A messianic psalm foretells the person and work of Christ before His incarnation.) What promises did God make to "the LORD," Jesus Christ (v. 4)?

5. Read Hebrews 7:11–17. (a) From what tribe of Israel did the Lord Jesus descend (v. 14)?

(b) How, then, is Christ qualified to be a priest as God promised Him in Psalm 110:4 (Hebrews 7:16, 17)?

In Hebrews 7:18–28 we see that a relationship with Christ is more excellent than a system of religion. The old covenant (testament) was based on keeping the law. The Israelites were still redeemed by faith, but that faith had to be expressed through observing a myriad of instructions that God's law required. It established a relationship with God by faith, but it could not provide the *power* to change hearts and to live obediently before God.

6. As stated in verses 18 and 19, what was the "problem" surrounding the system of law-keeping? (See also Romans 7:14–21 and 8:3 and 4.)

7. But now Jesus Christ has brought a new covenant (testament), based on *grace* through faith, which is far better than the old covenant. What is the advantage of the new covenant, established by His death, burial, and resurrection (Hebrews 7:19)?

8. Many religions today have priests, but Jesus Christ is the only priest we will ever need. Why is He the exclusive and eternal priest as expressed in these verses?

Verses 23, 24

Verse 25

Verse 26

Verse 27

Verse 28

9. A mediator is a go-between to bring two parties together. According to 1 Timothy 2:5 and 6, Who is the *only* acceptable mediator Who can represent us before God?

10. Review Hebrews 8:1–6. As the true, heavenly High Priest, Jesus alone is the mediator between God and man. Referring again to 1 Timothy 2:6 and Hebrews 7:26, what did Jesus offer up to God as a sacrifice for our sin?

11. Why is the new covenant, brought into effect by Christ's death and resurrection, better than the old covenant God made with Israel (Hebrews 8:6)?

12. Every manmade religion falls short of redemption and true, spiritual re-creation. Read Romans 8:28 and 29 and state the purpose for which God chose us and saved us.

According to Hebrews 8:7–13, the old covenant of law-keeping and sacrifice could not be totally effective because of sin. It only proved that man cannot save himself by living up to God's holy standards of righteousness. As a result God has put into effect, through Christ's death and resurrection, a new, more excellent covenant (Matthew 26:28; Hebrews 13:20). In Hebrews 8:10–12 the writer restated the promises of the new covenant given specifically to the Jews, God's earthly people, in Jeremiah 31:31–34.

13. What are these future promises of Israel's new covenant, based on Christ's redemptive work?

Verse 10

Verse 11

Verse 12

14. Similar promises have been given to the church, based on the everlasting covenant (Hebrews 13:20). What promises do believers, as God's heavenly people, have from God right now?

John 14:16, 17, 26

John 16:13, 14

Romans 8:4

Romans 8:15, 16

III. DISCOVER THE TRUTH

1. Should believers today give a tithe, more than a tithe, or less than a tithe? Read 1 Corinthians 16:2 and 2 Corinthians 9:7 as you consider your answer.

2. *Religious* giving is detached from spiritual significance. *Relationship* giving sees the correlation between God, money, and worldly goods. Abraham, who had a relationship with God, expressed a godly attitude toward himself in relation to worldly goods in Genesis 14:21–24. What is that attitude? What do you learn from his attitude?

3. To what other "mediators" do people sometimes look to represent them before God?

4. What are some of the things people might offer up to God today as a sacrifice to "cover over" their sins?

A religion is often a routine of practices that people perform in order to appease God—or so they think. Matthew 15:8 records Jesus' rebuke of the religious Pharisees. He quoted Isaiah 29:13, "This people draw near me with their mouth, and with their lips do honour me, but have removed their heart far from me." Relationship versus religion affects attitudes.

5. In each of the following categories, relate the heart attitudes that usually occur if we have *religion* as opposed to true *relationship*.

	Religion	Relationship
Prayer		
Bible		
Church Attendance		

Add any other observations you may have about religion versus relationship.

6. Eternal life is not just a future spiritual condition, it is a relationship of life with *the Life* right now. John 17:3 records Jesus' prayer, "And this is life eternal, that they might know thee the only true God, and Jesus Christ, whom thou hast sent." Do you really *know* God? How is the Holy Spirit working in your life to deepen your knowledge of God?

IV. CLAIM YOUR TREASURE

Has the Lord spoken to you through His Word? What decision do you need to make as a result of your study? Select one of the following decisions and spend some moments in prayer, asking the Lord to work in your heart as you seek Him.

_____ I have been trying to live my Christian life as a religion: dos and don'ts, trying hard to please God rather than abiding in my relationship with Christ. I want to walk with Him daily by grace through faith, trusting Him to lead and empower me to keep His commands. I realize that this is a growth process and will take time as the Spirit works this faith relationship in me.

_____ I have depended on a mediator other than Jesus Christ. I understand now, through God's Word, that He is the only One Who can represent me acceptably before God.

_____ My relationship with the Lord has become stale, deteriorating to a dry routine rather than a joy-filled life. I am asking God to work in my heart and renew my first love for Him.

V. REJOICE IN YOUR RICHES

We can know God! What on earth can compare with an opportunity like that? We can know God personally, fellowship with Him, call Him Abba, Father. Religion sees God as far away, with man stretching out his arm, which is too short to reach God. Our redemptive relationship sees God near, very near to us. His arms surround us; His hands hold us. He has reached out to us, and by faith in Christ alone we can draw near to Him. What can be more excellent than that?

Dear friend, don't settle for religion when you can have the treasure of a true relationship with God, your Heavenly Father.

Living a Life of Assurance

Hebrews 9 and 10

"Let us draw near with a true heart in full assurance of faith, having our hearts sprinkled from an evil conscience, and our bodies washed with pure water" (Hebrews 10:22).

During the 1400s and on into the 1800s, explorers searched for an elusive "passageway" from Europe to the Orient. Some sailed around Africa, while Columbus headed west across the Atlantic. This discovery would have brought him success—but he bumped into North America. In the 1800s Lewis and Clark battled against the upstream current of the Missouri River, hoping it would lead all the way to the Pacific Ocean. Despite all the seeking, the perfect passageway was never found.

The guilt that burdens a person's heart points plainly to the fact that she needs forgiveness of sins. The human race has devised many methods to try to "erase" sins and find a clear conscience, but every human effort falls short of eternal assurance. Only one way, one perfect "passageway," leads to a relationship with God: the redemptive work of Christ.

Is Christ's work sufficient to take away sins past, present, and future? Can it offer us a clear conscience? Can it assure us that we are loved and accepted by God despite our failings? Can it give us confident hope in an eternal dwelling place with Christ? The foundation of our whole spiritual life is redemption in Jesus Christ. His sacrifice for sin was the ultimate, superior sacrifice. As we rest in what He has done for us, we can live lives of victorious freedom and faith.

I. LOOK INTO YOUR HEART

Ask yourself the following questions.

Do you ever doubt your salvation?

Do you repeatedly remember past sins?

Do you pull away from God due to guilt?

Do you try to earn God's love and acceptance by your goodness?

Are you afraid of Christ's return?

Do you fear death and judgment?

II. SEARCH THE SCRIPTURES

Read Hebrews 9 and 10.

In Hebrews 9:1–10 the writer reviewed the regulations for worship that God had given to Israel in the Old Testament: the tent, divided into sections, and its furnishings (vv. 2–5); various ceremonies (vv. 9, 10); the high priest, who alone could go into the Holy of Holies only once a year, to offer animal sacrifices for the sins of himself and the people.

1. (a) What was one problem with this "temporary" system according to verse 9?

(b) The veil, or curtain, separated the Holy of Holies, where God's visible presence was, from the rest of the tabernacle. Of what was this veil a constant reminder to the priest and the people?

2. Hebrews 9:11–28 presents the Lord Jesus as both the Great High Priest and the perfect sacrifice. The Old Testament priest came before God in the Holy of Holies to offer a sacrifice for the sins of the people. But in this New Testament era, Jesus has offered Himself. What did the blood of Christ, shed on the cross, accomplish for us as stated in each of these verses?

Verse 12

Verse 14

Verse 15

Verses 22, 26

3. What two events must every person face (Hebrews 9:27)?

4. Priests offered millions of animal sacrifices under the Old Testament worship system. In what way is the sacrifice of Christ superior to animal sacrifices according to Hebrews 9:26 and 28? (See also Hebrews 10:10.)

5. Hebrews 9:28 mentions two appearances by Christ. The first time He came as our sacrifice for sin. As believers, we are expecting the Rapture, when Christ will appear in the air and take us to be with him in Heaven (1 Thessalonians 4:15–18).What should be our attitude toward that appearance according to Hebrews 9:28? (See also Philippians 3:20 and 2 Timothy 4:8.)

6. A clear conscience is a gift of peace and joy from God. The Old Testament sacrifices were a "temporary fix" until the time God would send His Son to die for us (Galatians 4:4, 5). What were some of the shortcomings of this system according to the following verses in Hebrews 10?

Verses 1, 4

Verses 2, 3

7. Hebrews 10:5–14 includes a quotation from Psalm 40:6–8, a reference to the Messiah. What was Christ's attitude when He came to offer Himself for our sins (Hebrews 10:5, 9)?

8. What was the result for us of the new covenant that was established by Christ's death (Hebrews 10:9, 10, 14)?

The new covenant, salvation through Christ's blood, is far more excellent than the old. Christ finished the redemptive work and is now seated in Glory (Hebrews 10:12). Believers are "perfected" (cleansed, acceptable, complete; Hebrews 10:14).

9. Moving on to Hebrews 10:15–22, we find that the provisions of the new covenant enable God to change our hearts (and Israel's in the future) by the work of the Holy Spirit (v. 16) and to remember our sins no more (v. 17). What other privilege has now been granted to us as explained in Hebrews 10:19–21? (See also Hebrews 4:16.)

10. How do these truths affect our relationship with God according to Hebrews 10:22?

11. The writer laid the foundation of our faith in Hebrews 5:9 and 10:1–22: the sacrificial death of Christ. With that unfailing foundation, our part is to diligently seek daily to walk "in Christ" so that our faith will bear fruit. What is expected of us according to these verses from Hebrews 10?

Verse 23

Verse 24

Verse 25

12. The fruit of faith in Hebrews 10:23–25 is the evidence of true salvation in a person's life. Sometimes a person makes a "profession" of faith that doesn't produce spiritual fruit. Read Hebrews 10:26–31. (a) When a person understands the knowledge of God's truth and chooses to reject His offer of grace, what must that person face (vv. 27, 30)?

(b) If a person rejects Christ's sacrifice for her sins, what other means of salvation is there (v. 26)?

13. Read Hebrews10:32–39. The writer praised the Hebrew believers for their faith. For what noteworthy conduct did he praise them in each of these verses?

Verse 32

Verse 33

Verse 34

Verse 39

14. What warnings did he give them in these verses from Hebrews 10?
Verse 35

Verse 36

Verse 38

III. DISCOVER THE TRUTH

The three great emotions that affect human behavior are fear, anger, and guilt. When a human being carries fear and guilt for her wrong-doings, it will affect mind, heart, and body. A person may try to "get rid" of her guilty feelings in many ways, but only God can provide a clean conscience.

1. (a) How can a person be free from the guilt of her sin? Review Hebrews 9:14, 26–28; 10:22; also see Romans 8:1; 2 Corinthians 5:17, 21; and 1 John 1:9.

(b) How can fear of death and judgment be removed? Find some Scripture verses that assure you that you need not fear death and judgment.

2. Jesus Christ is our great high priest and our perfect sacrificial substitute. He is the only way to a relationship with God. (a) What are some of the false ways that people seek to atone for their sins?

(b) How are these ways an insult to God?

3. Through Christ you have eternal assurance! God has totally accepted you. He will never love you less, no matter what. He could never love you more. He loved you before the creation of the world, and He will love you for all eternity (Ephesians 1:3–6). (a) What attitudes will cause you to daily "draw near" to God? (See James 4:7–10 for help.)

(b) What actions will cause you to draw near to God?

IV. CLAIM YOUR TREASURE

Has the Lord spoken to you through His Word? What decision do you need to make as a result of your study? Select one of the following decisions and spend some moments in prayer, asking the Lord to continue His work in your heart as you seek Him.

____ I have not been living with a clear conscience. I am confessing to God the sin that He has brought to my mind and putting it under the blood of Christ. If needed, I will seek to make things right with any person I have wronged.

____ I have not been able to draw near to God because I doubt His love and acceptance due to my failures. I understand now that because I am "in Christ," God totally accepts me because of His Son. I want to rest in His love and draw near to Him daily as my Heavenly Father.

____ I have not been holding fast the faith or evidencing fruit of my life in Christ. I want to recommit myself right now to walk faithfully with Him daily so that others will know I belong to Him.

V. REJOICE IN YOUR RICHES

In Hebrews 11 we will receive a great dissertation on faith. But chapters 9 and 10 lay the only foundation of our faith, the redemptive work of Christ. Without His death, burial, and resurrection, our faith would be futile (1 Corinthians 15:12–14). Without Him, we could not draw near to God. Without Him, we would live in dread of death and judgment. Without Him, we would languish over unforgiven sin. What a wonderful Gift! What a perfect Savior!

The old hymn by Charles Wesley so aptly expresses the truths of these chapters.

Arise, my soul, arise! Shake off thy guilty fears;
The bleeding Sacrifice in my behalf appears.
Before the throne my Surety stands—
My name is written on His hands.

To God I'm reconciled, His pardoning voice I hear;
He owns me for His child—I can no longer fear;
With confidence I now draw nigh,
And "Father, Abba, Father!" cry.

Seekers after the Eternal
Part 1

Hebrews 11:1–19

"But without faith it is impossible to please him: for he that cometh to God must believe that he is, and that he is a rewarder of them that diligently seek him" (Hebrews 11:6).

Searching for nothing. Wasted time. Some people seem to be on a trail of something extraordinary, but they come up empty. Some seem to foolishly seek what isn't there, and they find great reward.

Coronado, the Spanish explorer, searched greedily and restlessly to find "the lost cities of gold." But his endeavor was fruitless; no such cities existed.

In the 1800s a retired millionaire, Henrich Schliemann, decided to devote the remainder of his life searching for the ancient city of Troy that he had come to love from reading his favorite childhood stories. Scholars were skeptical that such a city even existed. But using Homer's *Iliad* as a guide, Schliemann began excavations and found the city he sought: nine levels of ancient Troy's ruins. His dream had become a reality.[1]

In this life you and I are searching for something. Our belief in our goals drives us on. But are you seeking for a vapor, that which will vanish away like a mist in your hand? Are you wasting your energy, your time? At the end of your life, will you come up empty or have great reward? The Bible relates to us the lives of many great seekers, seekers after the eternal. Though to the world they may have seemed to come up empty, great—very great—was their reward.

I. LOOK INTO YOUR HEART

What would you say is the overall goal of your life right now?

____ To please myself: to enjoy personal satisfaction, pleasure, and possessions.

____ To please others: to sense their acceptance and gain their attention and admiration.

____ To please God: to glorify Him and give Him my love and life totally, every day.

II. SEARCH THE SCRIPTURES

Read Hebrews 11:1–19.

Faith—true Biblical faith—is always the means by which we apprehend all that God has for us. This faith, as we have seen in the book of Hebrews, is always directed toward God through the person of His Son, Jesus Christ. Apart from Christ, faith is useless. Many people in the world have "faith," but it is not a faith based in the truth of God's Word, so it accounts for nothing. God tells us what to believe, and we must seek Him as He says.

1. Read Hebrews 11:1 and write a definition of faith in your own words, based on what God says it is.

2. Answer the following questions according to Hebrews 11:2.

    (a) Who had faith?

(b) What did it do for them? Explain your answer.

3. The writer of Hebrews then presented the accounts of the elders, the forefathers of the faith. He opened the Scriptures, as it were, to the book of Genesis. (a) What is the first fact of faith the writer mentioned in Hebrews 11:3?

(b) How did God do this?

4. Man is presented with a choice: live in a faith relationship with God or live unto self in the lust of the flesh. The effects of this choice were evident early in history in the lives of Cain and Abel, Adam and Eve's sons. Read verse 4. (a) What were the fruits of faith in Abel's life as stated in this verse as well as in Genesis 4:4 and Matthew 23:35?

(b) What were the effects of sin in Cain's life according to 1 John 3:12?

5. Read Hebrews 11:5 and Genesis 5:21–24. What were some of the evidences in the life of Enoch that he lived by faith in God? How did God especially reward him?

6. We should recall from Hebrews 3 and 4 that unbelief is a great sin because it fails to take into account the living God. Hebrews 11:6 presents the opposing mind-set. (a) What are some of the actions and attitudes that will be seen in our lives as we walk in true faith toward God?

(b) What is the promise for those who seek Him?

7. Read Hebrews 11:7 and Genesis 6:1–11. Describe the condition of society in Noah's day.

8. How is Noah described in these two passages?

9. Read Genesis 6:12—7:6; then read Hebrews 11:7 again. Explain why Noah's actions demonstrated great faith before the people of his day.

10. Read Hebrews 11:8–12 and 17–19. Abraham was a man who endured great trials of faith. What were some of life's testings, mentioned in Hebrews, that he had to face? (Also read Genesis 12:1–5, 15:1–6, and 22:1–19.)

11. (a) What were the attitudes and actions of faith that Abraham displayed in these testing times?

(b) What were the rewards of faith he received?

12. Read Hebrews 11:10. Explain what you think this verse means.

13. Look up the following references about "that city." What do you learn about it?

Hebrews 11:16

Hebrews 12:22

Hebrews 13:14

Revelation 21

14. Read Hebrews 11:13–16. This passage reminds us that when the great elders of the faith died, they had not seen all of God's promises completely fulfilled. Some promises were future; for example, the coming of the Messiah as foretold in Genesis 3:15. What was the mental outlook of these great saints toward God's promises as they walked their daily path of life (Hebrews 11:13)?

15. These faith-filled ones were seekers after the eternal. Their focus was on the big picture of God at work in the world, accomplishing His plan. According to Hebrews 11:13–16, what is the relationship between a seeker after the eternal and this temporal world?

III. DISCOVER THE TRUTH

1. How is belief in God as the Creator fundamental to a life of faith?

2. If a person accepts the theory of evolution, to what conclusion will she come (a) about the value of human life?

(b) About the value of a human soul (salvation)?

3. Proverbs 11:18 declares, "The wicked worketh a deceitful work: but to him that soweth righteousness shall be a sure reward." (a) What did Abel gain and Cain lose by their attitudes and actions toward God? Read Genesis 4:1–6 and Hebrews 11:4.)

(b) How do we, in a similar way, reap what we sow in our lives?

4. Noah was a seeker after the eternal; he was radically different in a time of darkness. How are we to be "salt and light" (Matthew 5:13–16) in the current time of darkness?

5. Abraham's life of faith was founded in the promises and character of God. If you read the entire Genesis account, you will find that neither Abraham nor Sarah had a perfect record of faith. Like them, we do trust God about some things while struggling with others. (a) What are some of the circumstances in which you find it difficult to trust the promises of God?

(b) What can you do at such times to strengthen your faith in God's Word and character?

(c) Abraham's response is recorded in Hebrews 11:17–19. How can our response in difficult cirumstances be like Abraham's?

6. Like Abraham, we can trust God's promises for the future. What are some of the promises you claim as you sojourn here?

7. We *can* please God. Enoch did. Read again Hebrews 11:6 and summarize how you must live in order to please God today.

IV. CLAIM YOUR TREASURE

Let's think again about these seekers after the eternal: Abel, Enoch, Abraham. Did they live to please themselves, to enjoy personal satisfaction, pleasure, and possessions? Did they live to please others to gain acceptance, attention, and admiration? No, these men lived to please God. They lived by faith, diligently seeking God and striving to obey Him despite human frailty.

In section I you answered a question about the goal of your life right now. If Hebrews 11:6 is now your goal, pray this prayer: *Lord, I confess that many times I live as if You don't exist. Often I don't have my eyes on heavenly things, but on earthly ones. Create in me a desire to seek after You. By the working of Your Spirit in me, draw me to Yourself and enable me to love and serve You above all else. Help me live by faith—real faith—today.*

V. REJOICE IN YOUR RICHES

Seeking God. Living for Heaven. Is it a waste of time and energy? Perhaps the world thinks so. But recall the words of our Savior: "What is a man profited, if he shall gain the whole world, and lose his own soul?" (Matthew 16:26). When Peter reminded Jesus that the disciples had left everything to follow Him, Jesus declared, "There is no man that hath left house, or brethren, or sisters, or father, or mother, or wife, or children, or lands, for my sake, and the gospel's, but he shall receive an hundredfold now . . . and in the world to come eternal life" (Mark 10:29, 30).

Second Chronicles 16:9 tells us, "For the eyes of the LORD run to and fro throughout the whole earth, to shew himself strong in the behalf of them whose heart is perfect toward him." Such was the case with Abel, Enoch, Noah, and Abraham. They were seekers after the eternal. Are you?

Note:

1. David Fisher, *World History for Christian Schools* (Greenville, SC: BJU Press, 1994), p. 51.

Seekers after the Eternal
Part 2

Hebrews 11:20–40

"Choosing rather to suffer affliction with the people of God, than to enjoy the pleasures of sin for a season" (Hebrews 11:25).

S eeing is believing." We've all heard that phrase, but you won't find it in the Bible. In fact, God encourages us to believe what we can't see, to seek the invisible.

Four hundred years before Christ, the Greek philosopher Democritus formed an idea that all matter was made up of minuscule particles that he called "atoms." Though he couldn't see these atoms, he believed in their existence. We now know that he was right.

Remember when Thomas refused to believe the testimony of the disciples regarding Christ's resurrection? Jesus chided him gently, "Because thou hast seen me, thou hast believed: blessed are they that have not seen, and yet have believed" (John 20:29).

We continue our walk down the corridor of the elders of the faith. We have considered the portraits of Abel, Enoch, Noah, and Abraham. These men all lived with their spiritual eyes focused on the invisible rather than the visible. Let's consider the faith of some other seekers after the eternal.

I. LOOK INTO YOUR HEART

As you examine your life right now, what would you say is your greatest spiritual obstacle to a life of deeper faith?

____ My own struggle with sin and personal inadequacy.

____ The lure of the world with its treasures and pleasures.

____ Fear of ridicule or being thought odd for obeying what God might want me to do.

____ Overwhelming circumstances; the failure of people around me.

II. SEARCH THE SCRIPTURES

Read Hebrews 11:20–40.

God had promised Abraham that He would bless his descendants and give them a wonderful land. Abraham and his son Isaac walked closely with God. But the fulfillment of God's promise looked a little shaky when Isaac's sons, Jacob and Esau, came on the scene.

1. Read Genesis 25:27–34 and Genesis 27. Describe the personality weaknesses of these two men.

2. Read Genesis 28:1–4. (a) Whom did God choose to inherit the promises He had made to Abraham?

(b) Why was this an act of faith on Isaac's part, as stated in Hebrews 11:20?

Read Hebrews 11:21. Over many years of testing and stretching by God, Jacob also became a seeker after the eternal. In Genesis 48 we read of Jacob's dwelling in Egypt because of a famine in the Land of Promise, Canaan. He had found his long-lost son, Joseph, and Jacob stood ready to bless his grandsons.

3. How did Jacob both worship and demonstrate his faith in God (Genesis 48:15–22)?

4. Read Hebrews 11:22 and Genesis 50:22–26. Many years later, Joseph and all the descendants of Jacob (Israelites) were still dwelling in Egypt. But the promise of God was not forgotten. (a) What faith did Joseph declare?

(b) How was this faith rewarded according to Exodus 13:18 and 19?

5. The next portrait presented in Hebrews 11 is that of Moses, the friend of God. Moses was God's chosen man to lead the Israelites out of Egypt and into Canaan. He was born into a household of faith. Read Hebrews 11:23 and Exodus 1:8—2:10. Faith is always God's answer for fear. How did God reward the faith of Moses' parents?

6. Read the summary of Moses' life as outlined in Hebrews 11:24–27. What choices of faith characterized his life?

7. The writer of Hebrews then enlarged his canvas to encompass the whole nation of Israel. In Hebrews 11:28–30 he spoke of three unusual acts of faith that Moses and the Israelites had to carry out in order to see the wondrous power of God. What were they?

Verse 28; compare with Exodus 11 and 12

Verse 29; compare with Exodus 14

Verse 30; compare with Joshua 6

8. The last specific seeker mentioned in detail in Hebrews 11 is Rahab. She was a pagan woman of Jericho who had heard of the miracles God had done for the Israelites as they journeyed back to Canaan. (a) According to Joshua 2:11, what testimony did she give of her faith?

(b) How did this faith give her courage and determination (Joshua 2:1–22)?

(c) How was she rewarded (Joshua 6:21–25)?

The writer of Hebrews must have realized he could never paint every Biblical portrait of faith for us; there are just too many. So he simply mentioned names to bring to our remembrance other elders of the faith. These names are listed in Hebrews 11:32.

9. Faith is called upon to meet many obstacles: our own doubts and fears, weaknesses, and inadequacies; overwhelming circumstances or the failures of people around us. The elders of the faith were real people with real trials. Select ONE of the following persons, read the passage, and tell what struggle the person faced. How did God strengthen his faith for his task?

Gideon (Judges 6:7–16)

Barak (Judges 4:1–16)

Samson (Judges 16)

Jephthah (Judges 11:1–11, 29–33)

David (1 Samuel 23:13–18)

Samuel (1 Samuel 16:1–13)

10. After naming certain people, the writer turned his attention to the acts of faith recorded in Scripture. Does faith in God always produce a favorable outcome from a human point of view? Sometimes the result is miraculous; sometimes it seems tragic. Read Hebrews 11:33–38 and categorize these acts of faith as positive or negative from our viewpoint.

Positive	Negative

11. What eternal blessings did these elders of the faith obtain in spite of what they faced in life?

Verse 35

Verse 39

12. These great followers of faith, along with us, will someday receive God's greatest promise of all. Hebrews 11:40 alludes to this truth. What is God's "better thing" that He will give us all?

III. DISCOVER THE TRUTH

1. The life of Jacob is a prime example that a seeker after the eternal may be far from perfect. The maturing of faith is a process that may take many years. Our continuing responsibility is to work *with* God, not against Him. Considering the life of Jacob, as well as other Scriptures, what are some of the means God uses to draw us, in faith, to Himself?

2. Living as a seeker after the eternal involves making wise choices, as Moses did (Hebrews 11:25–27). As a disciple of Christ, how have you had to make similar choices? Have these been easy or hard? Why?

3. Hebrews 11:27 tells us that Moses "endured, as seeing him who is invisible." Like Abraham, Moses saw the "invisible," God's realm, more clearly than the visible world. How must we do the same? Read Colossians 3:1–4. (a) How will this focus enable us to endure?

(b) What happens when we lose our focus on the Invisible One?

4. The Israelites had to do some "unusual" things to see the mighty works of God. What are some of the things God asks of us that probably seem unusual, even foolish, to those around us? See 1 Corinthians 1:18–23 and 1 Peter 4:1–5, 13, and 14.

5. Real faith fosters courage. Rahab had it, as did the named and unnamed people mentioned at the end of Hebrews 11. What situation has required courage in your life, and how has your faith provided that courage?

6. Scan the portraits of Hebrews 11 once more. Summarize the characteristics of a seeker after the eternal.

IV. CLAIM YOUR TREASURE

Look back at page 68, Look into Your Heart. What obstacle did you check? The greatest obstacle that you face right now in your spiritual life has also been faced by the elders of the faith. "There hath no temptation [trial, testing] taken you but such as is common to man: but God is faithful, who will not suffer you to be tempted above that ye are able; but will with the temptation also make a way to escape, that ye may be able to bear it" (1 Corinthians 10:13). God strengthened those Biblical saints who chose to walk with Him just as He will strengthen you in your trial. The hindrance is *unbelief* in God and His Word.

Read again Hebrews 11:6 and spend some moments in prayer, expressing to God your obstacle, confessing your sin, and requesting faith and strength. Find a verse to claim and continue to pray in unwavering faith.

V. REJOICE IN YOUR RICHES

"Hearken, my beloved brethren, Hath not God chosen the poor of this world rich in faith, and heirs of the kingdom which he hath promised to them that love him?" (James 2:5). Faith makes us rich; we have all things (Romans 8:32). Why seek for more? All we must do is believe what we cannot see. A. W. Tozer prayed, "Make Heaven more real than any earthly thing." If this is our prayer, then we, too, have taken a great step toward becoming seekers after the eternal.

The Focus of Our Faith

Hebrews 12:1–11

"Looking unto Jesus the author and finisher of our faith; who for the joy that was set before him endured the cross, despising the shame, and is set down at the right hand of the throne of God" (Hebrews 12:2).

I'm a bird watcher, and sometimes seeking that desired little object can be quite a challenge! I hear the bird and long to see it, but the endless tangle of branches and leaves, the glare of the sun, or the fuzzy focus of my binoculars hinders my objective. Occasionally, frustration has caused me to abandon my search. But often, with persistence, I can overcome the hindrances and be rewarded with the view of a beautiful specimen of God's handiwork that I haven't seen before.

As we learned in Hebrews 11:6, the Christian life is one of seeking after God. We, too, face hindrances: the endless tangle of life's sticky problems and demands, the glare of temptation and sin, our own emotions that frustrate us and make us want to abandon our search. Sometimes our focus is fuzzy, and we find we are concentrating on something other than our life in Christ.

The single object of our faith is Christ alone. It's up to us to sharpen the focus of our faith and see what God wants us to see: Jesus.

I. LOOK INTO YOUR HEART

1. Underline the emotion, if any, that is weighing you down right now.

worry   doubt   fear   anger

pride   jealousy   covetousness   self-pity

2. Name the particular sin, if any, in your life at present that easily besets you.

3. Circle the phrase that describes your current focus on Christ.

quite blurry   a little out of focus   sharp and clear

4. Are you undergoing a trial that is testing your faith?

II. SEARCH THE SCRIPTURES

Read Hebrews 12:1–11.

We have looked at the lives of the elders of the faith. In Hebrews 12 the writer turned the tables: we are being watched as we run the race of life. The witnesses (the forerunners of the faith) have finished their course; we are still toiling to finish ours.

1. In this marathon race of life, two problems plague us as we seek to run. What are these problems (Hebrews 12:1)?

2. In Hebrews 12:1 what are we told to do about these two problems?

3. Much of our emotional baggage comes from *wrong thinking* about the problems of life. What are some of the emotional burdens that we carry?

4. According to Isaiah 26:3 and 4 and Philippians 4:6–8, how can we replace our emotional baggage with the peace of God?

5. Romans 7 attests to the fact that the sin in our flesh may easily overcome us. But as believers in Christ, we now have a new nature that can respond to God, and we *can* overcome sin. Read the following verses and explain what they say about victory over sin.

Romans 6:12, 13

Romans 13:14; John 15:5

Galatians 5:16–25

6. According to Hebrews 12:1, how are we to run the race of life? What does this imply about the race?

7. Read Hebrews 12:2 and 3. These verses instruct us on what the focus of our "faith run" should be; that is, what will guide us to the finish line. (a) To Whom are we to look constantly as we press on?

(b) What is He called? What do these terms mean?

8. In what ways was Christ the ultimate example of a life of faith and perseverance (Hebrews 12:2, 3)?

9. To what did Christ look forward as He endured His pain?

10. As we "look unto Jesus" and "consider him," what will we be kept from doing (Hebrews 12:3)?

11. In Hebrews 12:3 and 4 the writer put the struggles of his readers into perspective by comparison. (a) With Whom did he want them to compare themselves?

(b) To what event may the writer have been referring? See Luke 22:39–45.

Hebrews 12:5–11 deals with the topic of chastening. When we become entangled in sin or take our eyes off the goal and begin to stray, God may have to chasten us. His chastening, of course, has many purposes: to cleanse us from sin, to teach us patience and endurance, to make us compassionate and merciful, to strengthen our faith.

12. Hebrews 12:5 and 6 quote Proverbs 3:11 and 12. What are two ways we might react to God's discipline in our lives according to verse 5?

13. It is not a whim that causes God to chasten us, but God's consistent character. (a) What attribute of God motivates Him to send discipline into our lives (Hebrews 12:6)?

(b) What relationship requires this discipline?

14. Our earthly parents disciplined us as they thought best, and hopefully we respected them for it. They may not have been perfect parents, but they sought to train us to become successful adults. God is the perfect Father; His training is never faulty. What ultimate outcome does God desire when He sends chastening trials into our lives (Hebrews 12:10, 11)?

15. (a) According to Hebrews 12:11, how will we react *emotionally* when God chastens us?

(b) Mentally and spiritually, how must we respond to any ordeal that tries us?

III. DISCOVER THE TRUTH

Imagine a person trying to run a race while carrying her luggage: suitcase, travel bag, garment bag, etc. Progress would be greatly hindered and energy quickly sapped! So it is spiritually, mentally, and emotionally when we choose to carry burdens in the race of life.

1. Select ONE of the following emotions and describe its devastating effects. Give a Biblical solution for laying that "weight" aside. Use references if you can.

Worry

Doubt

Fear

Anger

Guilt

Pride

Jealousy

Covetousness

Self-pity

2. God's Word reminds us that sin so easily besets us. What measures do you take to prepare a defense against sin's attack? What resources has God given you to enable you in that defense?

"What would Jesus do?" This has become a popular question in recent years. While we must always be careful not to think of Christ as just a good example but as Savior and Lord, He is also the pattern for our living.

3. In what particular situations of life have you "look[ed] unto Jesus" as the model for your conduct?

In times of trial we usually react with our emotions first. (We saw in Hebrews 12:5–11 that we might react with grief, resentment, or despondency.) After we acknowledge our feelings to ourselves and God, our immediate responsibility is to begin to put our thoughts in order, to respond by setting our minds and wills upon the facts of God's Word. This, in turn, will eventually guide our feelings. This order is important because we don't live by our feelings but by the Word of God.

4. What are some truths of Scripture upon which you lean in times of testing?

5. Jesus looked beyond the agony of the cross to the joy of finishing His Father's will. He knew that He had a victor's seat awaiting Him at the Father's right hand. To what future events that God has promised do you look as you persevere in your present race of faith?

IV. CLAIM YOUR TREASURE

Has the Lord spoken to you through His Word? What decision do you need to make as a result of your study? Select one of the following decisions and spend some moments in prayer, asking the Lord to work in your heart as you seek Him.

_____ In my spiritual life right now, I am being hindered by the emotional baggage of _____. I confess this sin to God and ask that the peace of God would rule my heart and mind as I think right thoughts based on Scripture.

___ I have been easily beset by the sin of _____.
I know that because I am in Christ, sin no longer has a right to rule me (Romans 6). I will seek each day to put on the Lord Jesus Christ (Romans 13:14) and walk in the Spirit's power (Galatians 5:16).

___ Lately I have been weary and faint of mind toward God. I want to refocus on Jesus, my Lord. I am asking Him to renew my strength as I consider Him each day.

___ I believe that God may be chastening me. I may be reacting with resentment or despair. I am asking Him to show me clearly what He wants to teach me, and I am committing myself to pray that righteousness and holiness will be the result in my life.

V. REJOICE IN YOUR RICHES

What better focal point for our lives than Jesus Christ? As we think back over the book of Hebrews, we have seen Him as the express image of the Father (1:3), the sinless man (2:14), our faithful high priest (chapters 3—5), the only intercessor (7:25), mediator of the new covenant (8:6), perfect sacrifice for sin (chapters 9; 10), and now, the author and finisher of our faith. Jesus is complete, and we are complete in Him.

The world tantalizes us with false promises of satisfaction. But Christ alone can bring true satisfaction, for He is all we need. Where is your focus? Whatever you're facing, look unto Jesus, and you'll need look no further.

Pitfalls in Our Pursuit

Hebrews 12:12–29

"Wherefore we receiving a kingdom which cannot be moved, let us have grace, whereby we may serve God acceptably with reverence and godly fear" (Hebrews 12:28).

As we have seen, in our search for God's greatest riches, we will have obstacles to overcome. Our own emotional burdens, struggles with sin, and weariness will hinder our seeking. But other pitfalls will be in our path as well. Will we stay on track for God, seeking to know Him better? Or will we stray and lose the reward? It's time for an attitude check. Are you ready?

I. LOOK INTO YOUR HEART

There's a caution sign ahead. Please slow down and evaluate carefully the direction in which you are running. The path on the left leads to regret; the path on the right leads to reward and rejoicing.

I feel like quitting.	I must go on.
I just can't stand that person.	Lord, help me love that person.
I want to enjoy what the world has to offer.	I want to put God first.
Not now, God.	I offer You, Lord, my life, my love, and my service today.
DEAD END	FINISH LINE

86

II. SEARCH THE SCRIPTURES

Read Hebrews 12:12–29.

1. In Hebrews 12:1–11 the writer used words such as "patience," "endurance," and "resistance" to describe what our mind-set is to be as we run the race of faith. (a) What is the condition of the runner (believer) pictured for us in 12:12?

(b) What things mentioned in Hebrews 12:1–11 may cause that kind of condition?

(c) What is the twofold remedy mentioned in Hebrews 12:1 and 2?

A pitfall is any danger, difficulty, or error into which one may fall unknowingly. As we run our daily race, we must be aware of pitfalls in our path. Satan especially wants us to stumble and fall. Once we throw off our hindrances and focus on the goal, Jesus Christ, we must run, always choosing straight pathways. We need to choose the pathway that is God's will for us and encourage ourselves with that knowledge when we meet peril and resistance.

2. (a) What does Hebrews 12:13 direct us to do?

(b) What is the reason for this action?

3. Hebrews12:14 presents two pathways. What are they?

4. One potential problem involves our relationships with people. Daily interaction with others may obstruct the pathway to peace. People are always popping up with their own particular temperaments, expectations, and philosophies. How are we to treat people according to the following verses?

Hebrews 12:14

Romans 12:17, 18

Colossians 4:5, 6

5. Next the writer turned his attention to several pitfalls in the pathway of holiness. What pitfall is described in Hebrews 12:15? How would you define this word?

6. Bitterness is likened to a wild, entangling, poisonous vine. What two precautions are necessary to keep from becoming entangled by it (Hebrews 12:15)?

7. (a) What spiritual problem is presented in Hebrews 12:16 and 17?

(b) Explain what you think this attitude means based on the example of Esau?

8. (a) What was Esau's reaction when he realized the consequences of his loss (Hebrews12:17; Genesis 27:34–38)?

(b) Did this change the consequences?

(c) Was this reaction true repentance?

(d) Why do you think he reacted this way?

Hebrews 12:18–21 is the writer's closing argument, which might be titled "This Most Excellent Gospel." Read the Hebrews passage and Exodus 19 and 20. God's holiness and judgment against sin is the central impression of this scene at Mount Sinai where God gave Israel His laws.

9. (a) What was the emotional response of the people to God's revelation of Himself at that time?

(b) What were God's chief objectives in revealing Himself this way (Exodus 19:9; 20:19, 20)?

10. Mount Sinai was a place of dread, and the Israelites were commanded to stay afar off. By contrast, believers in Christ under the gospel of grace are invited to "come." Rather than holding up His holy hand to keep us back, He now beckons us and wraps us in His fatherly arms of love. Read Hebrews 12:22–24. (a) According to verse 22, to what blessed spiritual place are redeemed people welcome to come?

(b) Who will join us there?

11. The Israelites were part of an earthly assembly. To what spiritual assembly do we belong as Christians (Hebrews 12:23)?

12. Read Hebrews 12:25–29. God is still judge, but as part of this spiritual assembly, upon what do we base our assurance of God's acceptance (Hebrews 12:23)?

Hebrews 12:24 points us to the pinnacle of God's plan: Jesus Christ. Moses was the mediator (go-between) of the old covenant between God and Israel. But now we look to Jesus, Who is greater than Moses (Hebrews 3:3), and to His shed blood rather than the blood of animals to remove our sin. God has revealed His rich plan of redemption through His Son.

13. Each person is faced with a choice: to fully believe and receive or refuse to believe and reject. (a) What warning is given in Hebrews 12:25?

(b) How do unbelievers refuse God?

(c) How do believers refuse Him?

Hebrews 12:29 refers to God as a "consuming fire." God has not changed since Mount Sinai; He is still all-powerful and holy. When He spoke at Sinai, He shook the earth. As the writer mentioned in Hebrews 12:26 and 27, at some future time God is going to catastrophically shake both the heavens and the earth.

14. (a) What will remain even when everything temporal is swept away (Hebrews 12:28)?

(b) In light of this fact, what are we to be doing right now?

(c) How can we do this acceptably?

(d) What attitudes are required of us as His children?

III. DISCOVER THE TRUTH

Hebrews 12:1–11 reminds us that in life obstacles will loom on the horizon. These obstacles include our own sinful choices and emotional reactions, spiritual persecution, and adverse circumstances meant to purify and strengthen us. But in facing these obstacles, we may develop bad attitudes. Bad attitudes arise from wrong thinking. Wrong thinking must be remedied by renewing our minds with Scriptural truth (Romans 12:2). If we don't, we end up "stuck in the pits" along our path.

1. Pessimism, chronic discouragement, quitting. Sometimes Christians drop out of the race and are spiritually disqualified. What kind of thoughts will cause a believer to give up seeking and serving God? In addition to the example, list three such thoughts on the left and offer a Biblical solution on the right.

Wrong Thoughts	**Biblical Thoughts**
1. I've sinned too much to serve God.	I'm forgiven and accepted by God (Ephesians 1:6, 7).
2.	
3.	
4.	

2. Hebrews 12:13 instructs us to "make straight paths for your feet." Every day we make choices that either honor or dishonor God, that facilitate or frustrate our spiritual walk. What are some of the choices you will need to make daily in order to accomplish the following directives given in Hebrews 12?

Follow peace with all people (v. 14).

Follow holiness (v. 14).

Extract any root of bitterness (v. 15).

Avoid being profane, or worldly-minded (v. 16).

Avoid stubbornness (v. 25).

Serve God acceptably (v. 28).

3. Esau traded his valuable birthright for a bowl of soup. Genesis 27 records that when he learned of his further loss of blessing, he reacted emotionally. But was he repentant and truly sorry? Note the following reactions of Esau. Then, beside them, explain how a person will respond if she is truly repentant with godly sorrow. (By way of contrast, read of David's repentance in 2 Samuel 12:1–24.)

Self-pity

Blame-shifting

No acknowledgment of sin

Revenge

Bitterness (grudge)

Busy! Busy! Busy! So many people are busy in the church, filling their weekly schedule with activity. Don't misunderstand, we *are* saved to serve and tell others (Ephesians 2:10), but first and foremost our focus must be on a right relationship with Christ. Then ministry and good works will flow forth from our lives through the power of the Holy Spirit. Anything else is not fruit, but works of the flesh. Read Hebrews 12:28 again and answer the following questions.

4. The Greek word for "serve" can also be interpreted as "worship." As you serve God, do you see it as an act of worship to Him? Explain.

5. "With reverence" means having a sense of modesty, realizing our humble position before God. (a) What attitudes, then, must be present in us as we serve and worship God?

(b) What attitudes would be offensive to Him?

6. What does the grace of God have to do with worshiping and serving in a way that pleases Him?

IV. CLAIM YOUR TREASURE

Put a check beside any wrong attitude about which God has convicted you through His Word. Pray about this attitude, and add it to your prayer list as well.

____ Spiritually, I have quit seeking God in my heart and mind.

____ I have not responded properly in my relationship with a particular person. I am asking the Lord to work His attitudes in me so that I can live peaceably with this one.

____ I have not cared about pursuing holiness. I need to get rid of _____ in my life and look to Christ to purify me from this.

____ I have been bitter against _____. I'm confessing this to God and choosing to forgive (whenever I feel angry again).

____ I have refused to listen to God about _____. Instead, I need to: _____.

____ I need to truly repent about my sin of _____ against God. I am confessing this sin to Him, taking responsibility and accepting the consequences.

____ I have been busy serving God, but only in my own flesh and strength. I will examine my motives and my spiritual source of power with regard to my ministries.

V. REJOICE IN YOUR RICHES

We've had much to consider in this lesson, haven't we? Some of the greatest obstacles we face spiritually are our own attitudes. Attitudes are thoughts that develop into patterns by repetition. Attitudes could be called "hardening of the 'heart-aries.'" Proverbs 23:7 states, "For as he thinketh in his heart, so is he."

Pessimism, irritability, self-centeredness, worldliness, bitterness, criticism, and complaining are attitudes that need to be broken. Have you been stuck in the pit of a bad attitude? The grace of God, which can meet all our needs, can release you as you truly repent and seek to serve and worship God.

Seeking a Life of Excellence

Hebrews 13

"Now the God of peace, that brought again from the dead our Lord Jesus, that great shepherd of the sheep, through the blood of the everlasting covenant, make you perfect in every good work to do his will, working in you that which is wellpleasing in his sight, through Jesus Christ; to whom be glory for ever and ever. Amen" *(Hebrews 13:20, 21).*

Have you ever been involved in a scavenger hunt? Each participant receives a list of various items for which she is to seek. The goal is to find every item listed and return "home."

Hebrews 13 is a list of things we need to seek. These items will "fine-tune" each Christian's life into a life of excellence. The writer reminded his readers of truths they had learned that now needed to be put into practice. The most excellent gospel, which came through our most excellent Savior, leads to a most excellent life!

I. LOOK INTO YOUR HEART

Here is a list of spiritual items you are to seek. How many do you have right now?

____ Brotherly love

____ A willingness to show hospitality

____ Sexual purity

___ A contented spirit

___ A daily trust in God

___ Respect for and submission to your pastor

___ A daily dependence upon grace

___ An unashamed witness for Christ

___ An attitude of praise

___ Good works unto God

___ Generous giving

___ A healthy prayer life

___ A willingness to do God's will

II. SEARCH THE SCRIPTURES

Read Hebrews 13.

In the first twelve chapters of Hebrews, the writer seemed to be an attorney, formally and forcefully arguing the case for Biblical Christianity as he stood before his readers. In Hebrews 13 he seemed to lay aside his lawyer's attire and clothe himself in the humble, well-worn garments of a pastor-teacher. He sat down among his readers as fellow-believers to gently instruct and exhort them.

1. (a) What instruction is given in Hebrews 13:1?

(b) Why is love among Christians of utmost importance (John 13:34, 35)?

2. What exhortation is given to the believers in Hebrews 13:2?

3. Hebrews 13:3 directs us to add certain people to our prayer list. Who are we to remember? How are we to feel toward them?

4. Hebrews 13:4 directs our attention toward marriage. What is God's view of marriage?

5. (a) What is God's view of sexual relations within the bonds of marriage?

(b) What does He think of sex outside of the marriage relationship?

(c) What two sexual sins are mentioned?

6. (a) According to Hebrews13:5, what is one quality that will characterize a life of excellence? Why?

(b) What should *not* characterize our way of life (conversation)?

Hebrews 13:6 seems to imply that the temptation to covetousness is caused by fear of man. Perhaps some of the Hebrew believers were looking to their financial and material security to protect them in times of persecution, or perhaps they feared losing their goods because of their beliefs.

7. Of what are we to remind ourselves when we are tempted to fear the financial future?

8. Read Hebrews 13:7. Consistency of life should be the goal of every believer. To whom are we to look as spiritual role models for our lives?

9. Again, what is the motivation for living a consistent and continual life of faith (Hebrews 13:8)?

10. In Hebrews 10—12 the writer dealt forcefully with the doctrines of Christ, redemption, and salvation by faith. What warning did he give in Hebrews 13:9?

11. The danger then, just like today, was to add works to salvation and sanctification. We are saved by grace through faith alone (Ephesians 2:8, 9), and we grow by grace through faith alone (Titus 3:8, 9). (a) What were some people falsely teaching (Hebrews 13:9; 1 Timothy 4:1–5)?

(b) What had this abstinence accomplished spiritually for those who practiced it?

12. Hebrews 13:10–14 is a review of the sacrifice of Christ on the cross, which accomplished everything for us. The cross is now our altar, and Christ is our sacrifice. (a) Just as He bore our sin and shame when He died outside the city, what must we now bear for Him (v. 13)?

(b) What is our motivation to bear up under suffering (v. 14)?

13. What are we to sacrifice continually for Him (Hebrews 13:15, 16)?

14. (a) As stated in Hebrews 13:17, what is to be our response toward pastors?

(b) What great responsibility do they have?

15. Believers are a family. On a personal note, the writer briefly interjected some "family" news and requests. Read the following verses in Hebrews 13 and answer the questions.
(a) What was the writer's request (v. 18)?

(b) What was his goal for his life and ministry (v. 18)?

(c) What was the writer's desire (v. 19)?

(d) What did he urge his readers to do (v. 22)?

(e) What encouragement did he give his readers (v. 23)?

16. A life of excellence is possible for every believer as we engage in heartfelt prayer. The writer poured out his heart's desire for the Hebrew believers in a sublime doxology. The focus of the power in Hebrews 13:20 and 21 is again the Lord Jesus Christ and His work on our behalf. (a) List all He is to us as mentioned in verse 20.

(b) What does He continue to do for us as we wait to see His face (v. 21)?

III. DISCOVER THE TRUTH

1. (a) In a close-knit group, such as a local church, what frictions develop that hinder brotherly love?

(b) What attitudes are necessary in order to "let brotherly love continue"?

2. Is Hebrews 13:3 relevant for today? How will you put this verse into practice?

3. The Greek word for "whoremonger" in Hebrews 13:4 is *pornos*. To be very blunt, how might we, as Christians, involve ourselves in pornography without actually committing fornication or adultery?

4. In what ways might we put our trust in money rather than in God?

5. How can we discourage covetousness in our hearts?

6. How have you seen God "working in you that which is wellpleasing in his sight"?

IV. CLAIM YOUR TREASURE

Here is the list of spiritual items from section I. Read it again, and commit to prayer one area in which you want God to work "in you that which is wellpleasing in his sight."

____ Brotherly love

____ A willingness to show hospitality

____ Sexual purity

____ A contented spirit

____ A daily trust in God

____ Respect for and submission to your pastor

____ A daily dependence upon grace

____ An unashamed witness for Christ

____ An attitude of praise

____ Good works unto God

____ Generous giving

____ A healthy prayer life

____ A willingness to do God's willl

V. REJOICE IN YOUR RICHES

Hebrews is a book deep in teaching, warning, and exhorting. What a comfort that such a challenging book ends with a strong prayer of assurance that in all these things, God is working in us to perfect us and bring us into conformity with His will! As we seek Him, He sanctifies us. And Jesus Christ, Who is the same yesterday, today, and forever, is all we need now and forever. "By him therefore let us offer the sacrifice of praise to God continually, that is, the fruit of our lips giving thanks to his name" (Hebrews 13:15). Are you rejoicing in *your* riches?

LEADER'S GUIDE

Suggestions for Leaders

The Bible is a living and powerful book! It is God speaking to us today. Every opportunity to learn from it is a precious privilege. As you use this study guide, be flexible. It is simply a tool to aid in the understanding of God's Word. Adapt it to suit your unique group of women and their needs. The discussion questions are optional; the answers are provided to clarify my intent and stimulate your thought. You may have an entirely different insight as the Holy Spirit illumines your heart and mind.

Each section of the study has a specific purpose.

The *introductory paragraphs* furnish background information and lead into the topic of that lesson.

The answers to the questions in *Section I* (Look into Your Heart) are personal and should not be discussed in the group. They will help prepare each woman's heart to receive God's Word as she does her own study.

Section II (Search the Scriptures) is aimed at studying the actual text of Scripture and understanding what it says.

The answers to the questions in *Section III* (Discover the Truth) should help to focus on various applications of the passage for that lesson.

Section IV (Claim Your Treasure) is not for group discussion. The suggested decisions are starting points for each lady to put God's truth into practice in her own life. You should close the session in prayer, asking God to bring lasting fruit from your study of His Word.

Section V (Rejoice in Your Riches) will help to seal in your mind what you have learned from the passage.

The effectiveness of a group Bible study usually depends on two things: (1) the leader herself and (2) the ladies' commitment to prepare beforehand and interact during the study. You cannot totally control the second factor, but you have total control over the first one. These brief suggestions will help you be an effective Bible study leader.

You will want to prepare each lesson a week in advance. During the week, read supplemental material and look for illustrations in the everyday events of your life as well as in the lives of others.

Encourage the ladies in the Bible study to complete each lesson before the meeting itself. This preparation will make the discussion more interesting.

Also encourage the ladies to memorize the key verse or verses for each lesson. (The verse is printed below the title of each lesson.) If possible, print the verses on 3" x 5" cards to distribute each week. If you cannot do this, suggest that the ladies make their own cards and keep them in a prominent place throughout the week.

The physical setting in which you meet will have some bearing on the study itself. An informal circle of chairs, chairs around a table, someone's living room or family room—these types of settings encourage people to relax and participate. In addition to an informal setting, create an atmosphere in which ladies feel free to participate and be themselves.

During the discussion time, here are a few things to observe.

• Don't do all the talking. This is not designed to be a lecture.

• Encourage discussion on each question by adding ideas and questions.

• Don't discuss controversial issues that will divide the group. (Differences of opinion are healthy; divisions are not.)

• Don't allow one lady to dominate the discussion. Use statements such as these to draw others into the study: "Let's hear from someone on this side of the room" (the side opposite the dominant talker); "Let's hear from someone who has not shared yet today."

• Stay on the subject. The tendency toward tangents is always possible in a discussion. One of your responsibilities as the leader is to keep the group on track.

• Don't get bogged down on a question that interests only one person.

You may want to use the last fifteen minutes of the scheduled time for prayer. If you have a large group of ladies, divide into smaller groups for prayer. You could call this the "Share and Care Time."

If you have a morning Bible study, encourage the ladies to go out for lunch with someone else from time to time. This is a good way to get acquainted with new ladies. Occasionally you could plan a time when ladies bring their own lunches or salads to share and eat together. These things help promote fellowship and friendship in the group.

The formats that follow are suggestions only. You can plan your own format, use one of these, or adapt one of these to your needs.

2-hour Bible Study

10:00—10:15 Coffee and fellowship time

10:15—10:30 Get-acquainted time

Have two ladies take five minutes each to tell something about themselves and their families.

Also use this time to make announcements and, if appropriate, take an offering for the babysitters.

10:30—11:45 Bible study

Leader guides discussion of the questions in the day's lesson.

11:45—12:00 Prayer time

2-hour Bible Study

10:00—10:45 Bible lesson

Leader teaches a lesson on the content of the material. No discussion during this time.

10:45—11:00 Coffee and fellowship

11:00—11:45 Discussion time

Divide into small groups with an appointed leader for each group. Discuss the questions in the day's lesson.

11:45—12:00 Prayer time

1½-hour Bible Study

  10:00—10:30 Bible study
  Leader guides discussion of half the questions in the day's lesson.
  10:30—10:45 Coffee and fellowship
  10:45—11:15 Bible study
  Leader continues discussion of the questions in the day's lesson.
  11:15—11:30 Prayer time

ANSWERS FOR LEADER'S USE

Information inside parentheses ( ) is additional instruction for the group leader.

LESSON 1

Section II—1. God sent Jesus to earth to speak to us, to communicate Himself to us.

2. Christ has been appointed by the Father as the heir of all things; He made the "worlds" (the Greek word literally means "ages"); He is the "shining forth" of the Father's glory and the express image of His person; He sustains the universe by His power; He purged our sins; He is sitting at the right hand of God; He is superior to angels and has a more excellent name.

3. First, Christ is the Son of God. He has a unique relationship with the Father, equal in power, glory, status. Second, the angels were directed to worship Christ, while angels are not to be worshiped (Rev. 22:8, 9). Third, angels are ministering servants, but Christ sits upon the throne of God's Kingdom.

4. Jesus is equated to God (Elohim) and Lord, both Old Testament names for the Father.

5. Creation.

6. Immutability; eternality. ("Immutability" is the quality of remaining the same, never changing.)

7. To seat Christ at His right hand and subdue His enemies. (*Discuss*: what does "right hand" mean here? Where is Christ now? When will His enemies be His footstool? Read these verses: Ephesians 1:20-23; Philippians 2:9-11; 1 Peter 3:22; Hebrews 2:8; Revelation 11:15-18.)

8. The job of angels is to minister to the saints (believers).

9. The warning is that we give very careful attention to what we have heard about Jesus Christ, God's Son, and who He is and what He has done as described in Hebrews 1.

10. (a) Salvation. (b) We are told not to neglect salvation. (*Discuss*: What does "salvation" mean?)

11. (a) The Lord Jesus spoke of salvation, eternal life, during His ministry. (b) The

disciples were commanded by Him to continue to spread the gospel of salvation to all men (Mark 16:15). God confirmed the apostles' teaching about salvation by miraculous signs (v. 4).

12. Man is to be the steward of God's creation on earth.

13. He was willing to temporarily lower Himself to man's position in the universe (lower than angels), associate with us, and die for us.

14. He died for our sins; that is, God poured out our punishment upon Jesus when He died on the cross.

15. We receive salvation by believing on Jesus Christ alone and receiving Him into our lives by faith.

16. *Verse 9*—He tasted death for us. *Verse 10*—He enabled us to share God's glory. *Verses 11-13*—He made us part of God's family. *Verse 14*—He destroyed the power of death and Satan over us. *Verse 15*—He delivered us from the fear and bondage of death. *Verses 16, 17*—He made reconciliation between us and God. *Verse 18*—He now can help us in temptation.

Section III—1. Possible answers include the following: He is the express image (exact representation) of God; He alone is worthy of worship; He created the heavens and the earth; He is called God (Elohim, v. 8) and Lord (Kurios, v. 10); He destroyed death and the Devil.

2. They are spirits, made by God. God alone is to be worshiped; even the angels themselves understand this, as in Revelation 22: 8 and 9. (*Discuss*: Why might people believe in angels but not seek to know God?)

3. The creation is temporal, not eternal. God is greater than any created thing, and as Creator, is to be worshiped by the creatures He has made. We must, however, treat the creation with respect because it is the work of God's hands. As stewards of it, we must take responsibility to care for it (2:7).

4. People may neglect salvation because they want to live for things and pleasure. They may not want to turn from sin.

5. Believers may neglect salvation by not growing in grace and the knowledge of Christ. They forget about the wonderful forgiveness God has given them.

LESSON 2

Section II—1. Jesus suffered; He was tempted.

2. (a) Jesus was faithful in doing God's will, in carrying out the plan of redemption, as a son over God's house. (b) It was necessary for Christ to be faithful in order to carry out God's total plan. (See John 17:4.)

3. We can also be faithful in holding on to the faith through all our sufferings and temptations, even as Jesus did.

4. We harden our hearts, provoke, and grieve Him.

5. *Numbers 20:7-12*—Moses was rebuked, not for his anger, but for his unbelief (v. 12), which led him to disobey God's commands and see himself and Aaron as the

solution to the problem. *John 20:24-27*—Thomas was rebuked because of his adamant refusal to believe what he could not experience with his senses. He did not believe God could raise the dead. (*Discuss:* How are we like Moses and Thomas as we face life's circumstances?)

6. It is called having an evil heart. It is described as departing from the living God.

7. We are told to exhort one another daily. This means to warn or encourage. (*Discuss:* Why does God want us to exhort each other?)

8. (*Background:* The Israelites were slaves in Egypt, and God did mighty miracles to cause the pharaoh of Egypt to release them. Moses led the people through the wilderness to the land of Canaan, which God had promised to give them. Discouraged by the report of ten spies who said there were giants in the land, the people refused to trust God and go into the land. God then said they must wander in the desert for forty years, and their children would be the ones to go in and enjoy God's goodness.) (a) The Israelites were guilty of hardening their hearts, provoking and grieving God, sinning, not accepting His Word. (b) We are to have godly fear lest we grieve God by our unbelief.

9. Unbelief. It is mentioned in verses 6 and 11.

10. *John 15:4, 5*—Abide in Christ. *Romans 12:1, 2*—Present myself to God as a living sacrifice. *Romans 13:14*—"Put on" the Lord Jesus Christ; keep myself close to Him in heart and mind. We put off the works of the flesh by putting on Christ moment by moment. *Colossians 3:1, 2*—Set my affection (mind/heart/will) on Christ and heavenly things. *James 4:7, 8*—Submit to God (my will) and draw close to Him (heart/mind). By doing so, I "cleanse [my] hands." I purify my heart when I hate sin the way God hates it.

11. God, Who knows all things, exposes our sin and unbelief through His Word.

12. It is alive (unlike any other book); powerful; "sharp" enough to cut through our spirit, mind, will, emotions. It judges our deepest thoughts, attitudes, and motives.

13. We are to go to the throne of grace. We can actually go before God's throne by prayer. Christ our Mediator is at God's right hand.

14. Our High Priest is great, heavenly, God's Son, sympathetic. He will give us mercy, grace, and help in our need.

15. (a) Hold fast our profession; that is, we should remain faithful to God. (b) This passage assures us that our Lord has provided the spiritual resources we need to live a victorious Christian life. (See also 2 Peter 1:3-8.) We have the Word of God to guide us in all situations (Ps. 119:105). We have the privilege of prayer (Matt. 7:7). We have Christ Himself living in us to be our wisdom and power (1 Cor. 1:30; Phil. 4:13).

Section III—1. (a) Lot, Saul, Solomon, and Demas are a few. (b) First of all, some people fall away because they are not truly Christians. We must be certain we are saved. Then, faithfulness to God takes diligence, watchfulness, and continued remembrance of the truth through His Word. It is our daily task to seek the Lord.

2. *Thoughts/attitudes*—Worry, fear, panic, greed, unthankfulness. *Words*—Boast-

ing, complaining, nagging, swearing, lying. *Actions*—Selfishness, restlessness, laziness, stealing, cheating, immorality.

3. *Bible reading/meditation*—Through the Word, God speaks to us. *Prayer*—By prayer, we speak to Him. The Word and prayer are our means of true communication with God. We cannot have a relationship without communication. *Regular church attendance*—Fellowship with believers is our source of encouragement and accountability.

4. We ought to be talking about our Lord and what He is doing in our lives. We can share answers to prayer. Listening to the burdens of others and offering Scriptural support is another means of exhortation.

5. Personal answers.

LESSON 3

Section II—1. To offer gifts to God and sacrifices for the sins of the people.

2. (a) Christ's prayer was heard. (b) God did not remove the suffering Christ was to face. (c) Jesus obeyed His Father's will.

3. He trusted Himself (His reputation) into God's hands (1 Pet. 2:21-23); He forgave those who mistreated Him; He realized God's faithfulness in carrying out His will and promises.

4. They were "dull of hearing." (The Greek word for "dull" means "slothful.") The readers were mentally lazy, unwilling to learn new truths.

5. (a) He used the illustration of babies being weaned off milk and being put on solid food. (b) They were still drinking milk. (A ten- or twelve-year-old who drank only milk would be weak, underdeveloped, and ill-nourished. We can transfer this thought to the spiritual realm!)

6. Growth takes place through learning the Word of God ("oracles of God," v. 12), specifically, learning what it says about righteousness (a right relationship between God and man, v. 13) and the application of Scripture to everyday situations of life as they arise ("exercised to discern both good and evil," v. 14).

7. (a) The goal is to move on to spiritual maturity (perfection). (b) Moving on means getting past the basics of Christianity (salvation) in our knowledge and learning the deeper truths of our spiritual walk with Christ. (*Discuss*: Why might some believers fail to progress past "salvation" in their spiritual lives?)

8. (a) The Lord views such believers as a fruitless, worthless garden, having removed themselves beyond God's blessing. (b) These people must bear the chastening of God whatever that "burning" might be. However, the believer does NOT lose eternal life. (*Discuss*: What does Christ expect from us in this life according to John 15:16?)

9. He commended them for their work, their labor of love in Christ's name, their past and present ministry to the saints.

10. (a) They should have diligence, hope, faith, and patience. (b) They were not to be slothful.

11. (a) God promised to bless Abraham and multiply his descendants. (b) Abraham patiently endured, waiting to see the fulfillment of God's promise. (c) He obtained the promise, beginning especially when Isaac was born. (d) He swore by Himself to show His absolute determination to bring about His promises.

12. *Numbers 23:19*—God does not lie; He does whatever He says He will do. *Nehemiah 9:7, 8*—God performs His Word because He is righteous. *Romans 4:20, 21*—What God promises, He has the power to carry out.

13. It comforts us in our trials; it anchors our soul.

14. Because Jesus took our sin and judgment, God can now pour out upon us all the grace He wants to bestow upon us as His children. When we are "in Christ," He removes condemnation and wrath and can fully do good to us and bless us.

Section III—1. (a) Fear of what God might ask them to do or give up; feeling that God will not let them do as they want; fear of failing God. (b) Fear is removed by studying the Scriptures, learning of God's character, and trusting in His love and goodness.

2. (a) Personal answers. (In every trial we can learn more deeply about the attributes of God. Sometimes we focus on what is truly important in life. We learn about ourselves, and perhaps see the sin in our lives more clearly.) (b) We hinder growth when we react to suffering with self-pity and bitterness or seek to escape it rather than face it. (*Discuss*: What means do people use to "escape" facing their difficulties?)

3. We might remember that many of the early church believers were slaves, not highly educated. (My grandfather had only an elementary-school education, yet he read the Word daily and was a godly man.) Some reasons might be distractions from the world, quitting when things get tough, not applying the Word to their lives (mental laziness, as previously implied in 5:11.)

4. Ministry is a source of fellowship, getting close to people and sharing their joys and their sorrows. Also, in order to minister to others in the Spirit's power, we must be in fellowship with Christ.

5. To look spiritual before others; to boost self-image; to have fun; to get out of the house; to avoid other responsibilities; to know what's going on in the church; feeling false guilt to do it ("there's no one else to do the job"); to earn God's love and favor.

6. To glorify God; to do God's will; love for God and others; response to a God-given burden; to use God-given gifts and abilities; to edify the church.

7. See the previous questions and evaluate your motives for serving. Pray much about it. Ask counsel from those in authority (e.g., parents, husband, church leaders). Consider if you can do this ministry and still effectively meet your responsibilities to others (e.g., spouse, children, employer). Seek God's will with an open heart.

8. Personal answers.

LESSON 4

  Section I—1. The only Biblically correct answer is 5.

  Section II—1. (A "type" is a Bible person, event, or thing that represents and fore-shadows truths of Scripture found elsewhere. For example, the daily sacrifice of a lamb for sin in the Old Testament pointed to the death of Christ, the Lamb of God, in the New Testament. So, the Old Testament sacrifice was a type of Christ.) Both Melchizedek and Christ were "priests" unto God Most High; both have titles of a King—King of Righteousness, King of Peace (Salem). Nothing is told of Melchizedek's ancestry or life, so in a sense he has no earthly parents, beginning or end of days. In His deity, Christ also was not of natural descent and without beginning or end. Both had an endless priesthood.

  2. Abraham gave tithes (10 percent of all he earned) to him.

  3. He received a blessing.

  4. Christ would be a priest forever, after the order of Melchizedek.

  5. (a) Christ was of the tribe of Judah. (b) He can be a priest forever because He lives forever. Although He is not a Levite, He can be a priest after a different kind, the order of Melchizedek.

  6. The law is good, but because of sin in our flesh, we cannot perfectly keep God's laws. If we break one law, we are guilty of all (James 2:10). We are powerless in our own strength to come to spiritual maturity.

  7. It brings us hope of being able to know and fellowship with God personally and to progress and live fruitful lives that please God (Col. 1:10).

  8. *Verses 23, 24*—He is eternal and will not die. *Verse 25*—He alone, as God, has authority to give salvation; He provided redemption for us and continually intercedes before the Father for us. *Verse 26*—He is one of us but also above us, not tainted by sin as earthly priests are. *Verse 27*—He offered up Himself as the perfect sacrifice; only once was He to do that. *Verse 28*—He has no infirmity (human flaw or weakness).

  9. Jesus Christ.

  10. He offered up Himself.

  11. The new covenant is established upon better promises. It assures us not only of salvation but also of victory over sin in our lives. (*Discuss:* What are some precious promises Jesus made to us in Scripture? See, for example, Matthew 11:28; 28:19, 20; John 5:24; 14:1-3, 16, 17.)

  12. To be conformed to the image of His Son.

  13. *Verse 10*—God will put His laws into the hearts and minds of His people; the people will be drawn into a relationship with God. *Verse 11*—The people will know the Lord in a personal way. *Verse 12*—There will be complete forgiveness for sin, not just a temporary covering.

  14. *John 14:16, 17, 26*—The Holy Spirit will be in us, and He will teach us the truths of God. *John 16:13, 14*—He will teach us of Christ and glorify Him through us. *Romans 8:4*—The Spirit will enable us to fulfill the righteous requirements of God's laws. *Romans 8:15, 16*—The Spirit brings assurance to us that we have an intimate family

relationship with our Father God. (For further reference, see Romans 8:10-16, 26, 27; 1 Corinthians 2:9-12; Galatians 5:22-24; 1 John 2:27.)

Section III—1. Tithing is not commanded for believers in the New Testament era. In 1 Corinthians 16:2 we are told to give as God has prospered us. Second Corinthians 9:7 says to give bountifully, as we purpose in our hearts, and to give cheerfully. So a tithe, though not necessary, is probably a good starting point. We should not give grudgingly but generously.

2. Abraham understood that God was the One upon Whom he was to depend for all his worldly needs. His priority was his relationship to God and his reputation before people: that all should know he walked with God. Even his material dealings reflected his godliness. (Note: Abraham gave tithes to God even though he lived before the Old Testament law was given.)

3. People may go to priests as mediators. Also, they may look to "saints" or even Mary, the mother of Jesus, to mediate for them. Remember, the Scriptures declare that Jesus Christ is the only mediator between God and man (1 Tim. 2:5).

4. Good deeds; morality; giving up something they like or have.

5.

6. Personal answers. (Leader, Don't force the ladies to openly share their answers

	Religion	**Relationship**
Prayer	Selfish, rote, or clichéd; confession of sin might be general, not personal and specific.	Filled with love and praise to God; true repentance and confession; expressing desire for God's will.
Bible	Ignored; quoted or read but not cherished; focus may be on the "letter" (commands) but not the spirit (Christlike attitudes).	Read with desire; personal application of its truths; meditated upon.
Church Attendance	May be done out of duty or guilt, not with joy.	Delight in opportunities for spiritual nourishment and fellowship with other believers.

to the first question. You may want to use it as a springboard for a general invitation for personal discussion with ladies who are not saved. Group discussion should focus on the second part of the question.)

LESSON 5

Section II—1.(a) It could not totally clear the conscience for past sins that needed to be forgiven. (b) The veil was a constant reminder that the people could not directly fellowship with God or freely come into His presence. Their sin was only "covered up." They were still separated from a high and holy God.

2. *Verse 12*—The blood of Christ obtained eternal redemption for us. *Verse 14*—It purged (cleansed) our consciences from dead works (trying to do good things to earn eternal life). *Verse 15*—We have received the promised inheritance. *Verses 22, 26*—It provides remission (removal) of sin.

3. Death and judgment.

4. Jesus died only once, and His sacrifice covers all sins. (*Discuss*: Since this is true, why are the following practices unbiblical: transubstantiation [the belief that during the Lord's Supper, the wine and bread change into the body of Christ] and acts of self-punishment to "pay" for sins?)

5. We should be anticipating it, longing for it.

6. *Verses 1, 4*—Sacrifices could not make the people "perfect," or complete, in God's eyes because animal blood could not remove sin. It was an inferior substitute for a man's blood. *Verses 2, 3*—The sacrifices had to be continually offered; therefore they did not give assurance of a clear conscience.

7. His attitude was one of submission to the will to God, giving His body over to suffering.

8. We are "perfected," totally acceptable in God's sight (Eph. 1:6). When we are "in Christ," God sees us as having His righteousness. Animal sacrifices could not accomplish this. (*Discuss*: What is "sanctification"?)

9. We can enter into the very presence of God through prayer because our High Priest has offered the sacrifice for our sins and is standing before God as an intercessor on our behalf.

10. We need no longer fear to fellowship personally with God; we can draw near. We need not doubt our acceptance with God but can have full assurance of faith. A believer can have a clean conscience and can live as a new creation, freed from sin's dominion ("bodies washed with pure water"; see also John 13:10).

11. *Verse 23*—We are to hold fast to our faith without wavering (steady progress). *Verse 24*—We are not to think just about our own faith but how we can motivate other believers to deeper love and service (Phil. 2:4). *Verse 25*—We are to regularly attend meetings of the local church so that we can encourage others.

12. (a) The person who rejects Christ must face the judgment of God (John 3:17, 18, 36). (b) The only way of salvation is through Christ (Prov. 14:12; John 14:6).

13. *Verse 32*—Enduring great suffering. *Verse 33*—Enduring great afflictions and befriending the persecuted. *Verse 34*—Having sympathy for suffering people and giving joyfully of their goods; having strong faith. *Verse 39*—Continuing on in the faith.

14. *Verse 35*—Don't cast away your confidence. *Verse 36*—You need endurance to keep doing God's will. *Verse 38*—Don't fall into unbelief; stay firm in the faith.

Section III—1. (a) When a person trusts Jesus Christ and His sacrificial death, God then sees that person as righteous; that is, sins past, present, and future are totally forgiven and removed by Christ's blood. Daily confession of sin (1 John 1:9) keeps us in fellowship with our Heavenly Father. Asking forgiveness of others and making restitution give us a clear conscience with our fellowman. (b) Fear of death and judgment are also removed when we receive Christ as Savior. Though we still must face physical death, it is but a door into God's presence, an eternity of bliss. Read 1 Corinthians 15:53-55, 1 Thessalonians 5:9-11, and 1 John 4:15-18. (*Discuss:* What are the benefits of a clear conscience? Why do we sometimes resist dealing with our guilt God's way? What can we do if we are plagued by *false* guilt about past, confessed sin?)

2. (a) False ways are doing good works to earn salvation or trying to be good (Isa. 64:6); doing penance; joining or going to church; giving to charity; being baptized (Titus 3:5-7). (b) All religions that deny the full deity of Christ are false ways to God (Acts 4:12); and all cults and religions that teach salvation by self-effort or works are proclaiming a false gospel (Gal. 1:9). The true gospel is salvation by faith alone through God's grace alone through Christ's sacrifice alone (Eph. 2:4-9).

3. (a) Humility will cause you to see your utter need for God every moment. Hatred of sin will drive you to God for cleansing and for keeping you from sin's attacks. (b) Prayer, meditation on God's Word, praise, and serving God and others are actions that will help you draw near to God.

LESSON 6

Section II—1. Personal answers. One way to express the definition is, "Faith is being so sure of what we do not see, that, nevertheless, we not only believe it, but we act upon it."

2. (a) The elders; that is, the great patriarchs (and matriarchs) of the faith, especially as related to us in the Old Testament accounts. (b) Because of their faith, they obtained a good report. Maybe we should think of them as being A students on God's report card because they believed in Him with all their might!

3. (a) God created the worlds (in Greek, literally, "ages"). (b) God brought about the universe and His plan for it simply by speaking His word.

4. (a) Abel desired to obey God. His offering pleased God, and he was considered righteous because of his faith. (See Romans 4:3-5.) (b) Cain's works were evil, and he was under the control of Satan.

5. Enoch walked with God and pleased Him. He had a positive testimony for the Lord in his day. God rewarded him by "translating," or rapturing, him; that is, taking him to Heaven without the death experience.

6. (a) We will please God, as Enoch did; we will come to God; we will believe that He is and will act as if He exists at all times; we will diligently seek Him. (b) God will reward those who seek Him. (*Discuss:* Despite what we claim, how do Christians some-

times act as if God doesn't exist?)

7. Great wickedness; men's thoughts almost continually evil; grieving God; corruption; violence.

8. Noah found grace in the Lord's sight. He was a just man, perfect in his generation. He walked with God. By his faith he was righteous before God, and because he feared God, he obeyed God's commands.

9. He was doing something people could not understand. Noah tried to explain to them God's impending judgment (2 Pet. 2:5). Noah believed God's word and acted in accord with it. The people probably thought he was crazy, building a huge box in the desert. But his faith saved him when others scoffed and perished.

10. He was told by God to take all he owned and move to a faraway land. He then dwelt in a foreign country among people he didn't know. He and Sarah had no children to be heirs. But when God finally gave them a son, He then asked Abraham to sacrifice this precious son on an altar.

11. (a) He obeyed (v. 8); he believed (v. 19); he offered up his best to God (v. 17). (b) He was rewarded with an inheritance from God, a land (vv. 8, 9), innumerable descendants (v. 12), all the promises God had made to him (Gen. 12:2, 3), and a son.

12. Personal answers. Here is one possible explanation: Abraham, the father of the faithful, lived his earthly life with his eyes on Heaven. He believed that, upon his death, God would take his soul to an eternal dwelling, a celestial city, that would far exceed any worldly wealth. Christ gave us, His disciples, a similar promise in John 14:1-3.

13. *Hebrews 11:16*—It is a heavenly city in a better country, prepared for us by God. *Hebrews 12:22*—It is the city of the living God and the place where angels dwell. *Hebrews 13:14*—Unlike the cities of the earth that will pass away, it is an eternal city, yet to come. *Revelation 21*—It is a holy city without sin; it is where the visible presence of God will dwell with us forever; no sorrow or pain are there; we will, as God's children, be heirs; it is beautiful beyond description, full of God's light and glory; it is a secure city; it is only for those whose names are written in the Lamb's Book of Life.

14. They realized that the total fulfillment of God's plan reached beyond their own years on earth, but they deeply believed that God was real (Heb. 11:6) and that He would continue to work after they died. The verse tells us that they saw the promises afar off (faith), were persuaded of them, and embraced them. This was a total life commitment on their part to live for God.

15. Seekers are like strangers and pilgrims in this world. (See 1 Peter 2:11.) They are "passing through" to a better place. God and His Word are of the utmost importance. They use the things of this world, but they don't cling to them. By continually turning their backs to the allurements of the world and setting their faces toward eternity, they demonstrate their faith and love for God, and He, in turn, demonstrates His faithfulness and love for them (Heb. 11:16).

Section III—1. The Bible declares innumerable times that God created the heavens and the earth. If we don't believe that, we do not believe God's Word in any other matter. Second, if God is our Creator, then we are accountable to Him. If not, we feel free to disregard Him. Third, we learn of God's attributes through His creation; e.g., power, wisdom, sovereignty, faithfulness. We know we can trust Him.

2. (a) Belief in evolution logically leads to a devaluing of human life. If every human is a "chance happening," then there is nothing uniquely valuable about that life. Abortion, euthanasia, and leniency against murder are several results of our society's belief in evolution. The idea of survival of the fittest despises the weak. (b) There is no need for salvation. Since man is little more than an evolved animal, the eternal state of the soul is not important. Life is here and now. (*Discuss:* If a person has been taught to believe evolution, how can he or she come to accept creation?)

3. (a) Cain's attitudes and actions brought him a life of trouble. He was cut off from God in this life and had no eternal hope waiting for him after death. He lived for the now and robbed himself of eternal riches. Abel died young but had eternal treasure and a continuing godly influence on believers of all time. (b) We may also live for today and lose eternal reward or live daily for God by faith and look forward to His commendation (1 Cor. 3:13-15).

4. As Christians, if we are living lives of obedient faith, we will inevitably have attitudes, words, and actions that are different from the unsaved people around us. This will attract their attention. Some will ignore or even mock us, but some might be attracted to the "light." (*Discuss:* Find other similarities between our calling and Noah's. What persecution might we face that he faced?)

5. (a) Personal answers. (b) We can remember past deeds of God's greatness (as the Israelites did); meditate on Scripture; pray honestly about our struggles and fears. We can ask the Holy Spirit to strengthen us in our inner being (Eph. 3:16-21). (c) As Abraham, we can dwell upon God's power, faithfulness, and goodness. Also, fellowship with others who encourage us by their faith.

6. Personal answers.

7. Personal answers.

LESSON 7

Section II—1. Esau was emotional, impetuous, revengeful, without self-control, focused on the physical. Jacob was sly, calculating, deceitful.

2. (a) Jacob. (b) There was bad blood between the brothers, and Isaac had to send Jacob away. Isaac had to trust that God would somehow bring Jacob back to the Land of Promise. Jacob didn't seem inclined to seek a relationship with the Lord at that time.

3. Jacob praised God for all His care; blessed the younger son of Joseph over the firstborn, as God directed him; trusted that God would bring his descendants back into Canaan even though Jacob would not live to see it.

4. (a) That God would cause all of them to leave Egypt and return to the land He promised to Abraham, Isaac, and Jacob. (b) The Children of Israel left Egypt, taking

Joseph's bones, and returned to Canaan.

5. Moses' life was spared. He was found by Pharaoh's daughter, yet given back to his own mother to be raised for several years.

6. Moses was in a position to choose to be among the people of God or the people of Egypt. He chose to belong to God. He passed up pleasures, riches, esteem, and power to gain God. He chose suffering over comfort, affliction rather than affluence. Like his parents, he trusted God instead of his own fears and focused on the invisible over the temporal. (*Discuss:* Why is love of the world such a snare for Christians? What happened to Demas in 2 Timothy 4:10?)

7. *Verse 28*—Sprinkling a lamb's blood on the doorposts so that the death angel would pass over them. *Verse 29*—Passing between the walls of water of the Red Sea that God opened up for them. *Verse 30*—Walking around the city of Jericho for seven days until God made the walls crumble in order for them to capture the city.

8. (a) Rahab believed that the Lord is God of Heaven and earth. (b) Because she believed, she hid the Israelite spies and asked them for protection for her and her family. (c) Her life was spared, and she was given a dwelling place among the people of God.

9. *Gideon* was discouraged to see his people beaten down. He felt abandoned by God, and he saw himself as a nobody. How could he serve God? But God saw Gideon's potential as a man of valor. Twice He assured Gideon He would be with him. He promised His presence and power. *Barak* had great doubts about his ability to defeat Sisera's army. God assured him through His word (spoken by judge Deborah) that he would prevail. *Samson* had moral weaknesses and sinned. At the end of his life, he returned to God and prayed. God answered his prayer. *Jephthah* had to forgive the people of his own clan and town who had despised and rejected him. The Holy Spirit strengthened Jephthah for his task, and he trusted God to deliver them. *David* had been promised by God that he would be king, yet King Saul, David's rival, was trying to kill him. The Lord delivered David from every attack. He also sent David a loyal, godly friend, Jonathan, for support and encouragement. *Samuel* had anointed the first king of Israel. Now he was grieving over the disappointment of King Saul's failures. The Lord gave him guidance in choosing a new king and assurance of His control.

10. *Positive:* Subdued kingdoms, wrought righteousness, obtained promises, stopped lions' mouths, quenched fire, escaped sword, made strong, waxed valiant in fight, turned back enemies, raised dead. *Negative:* Sawn asunder, tortured, cruel mockings, scourgings, bands, imprisonment, stoned, tempted, slain, wandered destitute, afflicted, tormented, homeless. (*Discuss:* What do these results teach us?)

11. *Verse 35*—A better resurrection. *Verse 39*—A good report with God because of their faith.

12. God has given all of us the promise of resurrection bodies and of eternity with Him and His Son. (*Discuss:* What does Hebrews 11:13 mean in stating, "Not having received the promises"? When will we all receive the full promises of God?)

Section III—1. He uses people, good and wicked. (Laban, Jacob's father-in-law, was as crafty as Jacob and continually put obstacles in Jacob's way. This eventually turned Jacob's trust to God instead of himself.) God also uses pressing circumstances and trials to develop our faith. (See Psalm 119:67, James 1:2-4, and 1 Peter 1:6 and 7.)

2. Personal answers.

3. (a) We realize day by day that Christ is real, and this fact affects every area of our lives. It enables us to endure because every promise and principle of God's Word is true. I will see Him and give an account to Him. (b) When we stop seeking Him (Heb. 11:6), we fall off gradually.

4. Believe on Christ's death for our salvation; be willing to suffer, even rejoice in it, for Christ's sake.

5. Personal answers.

6. A desire to obey God (Abel); please Him and walk with Him (Enoch, Noah); a trust that acts upon God's Word and promises (Noah, Joseph, Abraham); a willingness to give up everything for God (Abraham, Moses); a surrender of one's life to God rather than self-sufficiency (Jacob); courage to do what seems foolish or even illogical and dangerous if it means obedience to God's commands (Noah, Israel); focus upon spiritual issues over temporal (all).

LESSON 8

Section II—1. The first could be called "carrying baggage." In the Greek, they are weights, burdens, hindrances. The second is the sin that entangles us. Interestingly, the Greek expresses it as "a competitor thwarting a racer in every direction."

2. Lay them aside.

3. Worry, doubt, fear, bitterness, guilt, pride, jealousy, covetousness, self-pity.

4. By keeping our minds focused on God and trusting Him. We need to commit our problems to God in prayer, be thankful, and think upon the good in every situation.

5. *Romans 6:12, 13*—We must choose to no longer be servants of sin, but servants of God. We must yield ourselves and our whole bodies to be God's instruments (Rom. 12:1, 2). *Romans 13:14; John 15:5*—Put on (or abide in) the Lord Jesus Christ, Who alone can enable us to put off sin. We have no power over sin, but He does. *Galatians 5:16-25*—Walk in (or yield to) the Spirit's power. He will restrain sin in us and produce righteousness. This is really the same as abiding in Christ. It is a moment-by-moment relationship of faith with the Triune God.

6. With patience (endurance, perseverance). It implies that the race will not be easy, and we'll be tempted to quit.

7. (a) Jesus. (b) He is called the author (originator) and finisher (one who brings something to the goal so as to win and receive the prize) of our faith. Christ is the Alpha and Omega in our lives. Without Him, we could have no faith in God because He is the Logos (revealer of God), Redeemer, and Enabler to live a life of faith (Gal. 2:20). We are assured that Christ will keep us saved (eternal security) and, as we cooperate with Him,

bring us to spiritual maturity.

8. Christ faced great opposition, accusation, and scorn, yet He finished the work God gave Him to do. In His death, He trusted the Father and yielded Himself to God's will, agonizing though it was.

9. The joy of finishing well and the fulfillment of God's promise that Christ would sit at God's right hand when all was accomplished.

10. Becoming mentally weary and giving up. (The summary of the elders of Hebrews 11 and the example of Christ in Hebrews 12 are meant to encourage us not to quit. See Hebrews 10:23, 35-39, which serves as an introduction to the passage.)

11. (a) Christ. (b) Jesus' praying in the Garden of Gethsemane.

12. Resentment and anger; fainting in the mind (giving up).

13. (a) Love. (b) He is our Heavenly Father; we are His children.

14. Our benefit—so we might become partakers of His holiness and enjoy the fruit of righteousness.

15. (a) We will grieve. (That grief might evoke anger or despair, v. 5.) (b) We must accept it (v. 7); be yielded to what He wants to teach us.

Section III—1. *Worry* eats away our peace, causes stress and physical side effects; Matthew 6:27-34; Philippians 4:6-8. *Doubt* causes us to stop trusting God, to look to ourselves and give way to fear; James 1:6-8. *Fear* paralyzes our faith and keeps us from serving God. Focus on God's character; Isaiah 40. *Anger* (resentment) lashes out at others and nurses our hurts. Submit, forgive, and let go; Ephesians 4:31, 32. *Guilt* keeps us from drawing near to God, accepting and forgiving ourselves; 1 John 1:9. *Pride* separates us from the grace of God. He will have to break our pride; James 4:6-10. *Jealousy and covetousness* cause hate for others, discontentment and ingratitude; Hebrews 13:5. *Self-pity* robs us of joy, makes us self-centered and ungrateful. We don't serve others; Philippians 2:4, 5.

2. Personal answers. God's Word renews my mind so that I know what is sin and what pleases God (Rom. 12:2). Christ's death and resurrection assure me of victory over sin and give me the understanding that sin no longer has the right to rule over me (Rom. 6). I have a new nature that is fully able to respond in righteousness (2 Cor. 5:17; Phil. 2:13). God has put the Holy Spirit inside me to live out the life of Christ (Rom. 8:1-14; Gal. 5:16-25). I can pray for grace in times of trial (Heb. 4:16).

3. Personal answers.

4. Personal answers.

5. Personal answers. (Examples: hearing "well done, thou good and faithful servant"; going to the place Christ has prepared; being at the Marriage Supper of the Lamb.)

LESSON 9

Section II—1. (a) The runner is worn out, ready to quit. (b) Wrong emotions and sin may make us weary. We may have wrong reactions to God's chastening. (c) We need to get rid of hindrances and focus on Christ.

2. (a) Make straight (good, upright) paths for our feet. (b) The reason given is "lest that which is lame be turned out of the way; but let it rather be healed [restored]." Weaker, struggling Christians may be watching us and following our example. Even if we manage to avoid the pitfall, they may not and it could devastate them spiritually. We are not to be stumbling blocks but are to help others by how we live.

3. Peace and holiness.

4. *Hebrews 12:14*—Follow peace with all men. *Romans 12:17, 18*—Don't repay evil with evil; be fair and honest; as much as you can, live at peace with all (avoid friction). *Colossians 4:5, 6*—Walk in wisdom; that is, think about how your attitudes and actions will affect others' opinions of Christ. Be gracious in your speech.

5. Bitterness. It may be called harbored anger, unforgiveness, or resentment.

6. Looking diligently into our own hearts for the root of it; experiencing the grace of God to overcome it.

7. (a) Spiritual fornication or being a profane person. (A profane person is one who is devoid of sensitivity toward God.) (b) Based on Esau's example, it is someone who forfeits the blessing of a relationship with God for earthly satisfaction. Unlike Abraham, Isaac, and Jacob, described in Hebrews 11, Esau didn't value the covenant promises of God that were his by his birthright as oldest son; rather he exchanged them for temporal things. Spiritual gain is of no value to this type of person.

8. (a) Bitter weeping. (b) No. (c) Based on the rest of Esau's life, it seems evident that his was not true spiritual repentance (i.e., I'm sorry that I sinned against God) but worldly, self-centered sorrow (i.e., I feel bad because what I did was bad for me!). (d) We can tell Esau didn't truly repent because he did not acknowledge his sin, he shifted the blame, and he sought revenge.

9. (a) Terror; they couldn't really endure it. (b) God wanted them to trust and obey Moses' leadership; He wanted them to avoid sin.

10. (a) To Mount Zion, a figurative name for Jerusalem; but this is the heavenly Jerusalem mentioned by the writer before in Hebrews 11:10 and 16. (b) An innumerable company of angels.

11. The church of the firstborn.

12. Our names are written in Heaven. We are justified (declared righteous) and seen as "perfect" in Christ. (*Discuss:* How can a person be sure her name is written in the heavenly books? Of what does having one's name written down assure us? See Luke 10:20 and Revelation 20:12.)

13. (a) Do not refuse. (b) By rejecting His gift of salvation. (c) By turning away from Christ and living again in sin's bondage.

14. (a) The kingdom of God. (b) Serving God. (c) By grace. (d) Reverence and godly fear.

Section III—1. Personal answers. (*Discuss:* What kept Paul going in Philippians 3:7-14?)

2. Personal answers, but here are some possible answers. *Follow peace*—Show consideration toward people (Phil. 4:5); exercise wisdom in your dealings with others

(Col. 4:5). *Follow holiness*—Spend time daily with God in His Word and in prayer (Ps. 119:11; Eph. 6:11, 18). *Extract any root of bitterness*—During times of confession and prayer, ask the Holy Spirit to show you unresolved anger you may be storing in your heart (Ps. 139:23, 24). *Avoid being profane*—If things or pleasures absorb your attention more than God, you may have idols in your heart (1 John 2:15-17; 5:21). *Avoid stubbornness*—Give in; yield your will to another's (Eph. 5:21; Phil. 2:3, 4). *Serve God acceptably*—Direct glory to God for all you do (Col. 3:17).

3. *Self-pity*—A truly repentant person does not feel sorry for self but for having sinned against God. *Blame-shifting*—True repentance brings acceptance of responsibility for the sin committed and its consequences. *No acknowledgment of sin*—The sinner will confess her sin to God, and if needed, to others she has sinned against. *Revenge*—True repentance humbly accepts the consequences and leaves all judgment with God; it focuses on what she must do to restore fellowship with God. *Bitterness (grudge)*—The repentant person will forgive as God has forgiven her.

4. Personal answers.

5. (a) Humility is needed to cause us to be dependent upon God as we serve. There will be joy and thankfulness as we realize the privilege we have to serve Him. (b) Offensive attitudes would be pride and boasting, selfishness (*my* ministry), contentiousness, or complaining.

6. The grace of God gives the enabling to serve through our weakness (Eph. 2:8-10, 1 Tim. 1:12), as we are filled with the Word of God (2 Tim. 3:16, 17) and the Spirit of God (Eph. 5:9). (See also 2 Corinthians 12:9.)

LESSON 10

Section II—1. (a) Let brotherly love continue. (The Greek word for "love" is *philadelphia*, which is the love of believers for one another.) (b) Love among believers authenticates the claims of Christ to the unbelieving world. It is that which most forcefully argues our case for the gospel truth.

2. Always be ready and eager to show hospitality to others as Abraham did in Genesis 18. (Recall that in Bible times travelers often stayed in the homes of common folk. What a great opportunity to witness for Christ!)

3. Those who are in bonds (prison) for Christ's sake, and those who are persecuted. We are to feel as if we are the ones being persecuted or imprisoned since we are one body.

4. Marriage is honorable. (The Greek word means valued, esteemed, precious.)

5. (a) They are pure and right. (The Greek word for undefiled is *amiantos* and means "having nothing in it which defiles." It is the same word used in Hebrews 7:26 to describe Christ!) (b) Outside of marriage, sex is wrong and will be judged. (c) Fornication and adultery. We need to keep the "marriage bed" pure: husband and wife only.

6. (a) We are to be content because God is with us, and He is all we need.

(b) Covetousness.

7. God is my helper. I will look to Him and not to man.

8. Those who rule over us (pastors, deacons, etc.), who teach us God's Word and demonstrate their faith by godly lives.

9. Jesus Christ, Who never changes. We can look to Him for all we face and need.

10. Not to be caught up in beliefs that are not Biblical.

11. (a) Some people were teaching to abstain from meat and from marriage in order to please God. (b) It had not profited them at all. (*Discuss:* Christians must have godly standards of behavior in order to separate from worldliness and be a light for Christ. But at what point may dos and don'ts become legalistic and a detriment to one's spiritual life?)

12. (a) His reproach. (b) Our eternal reward.

13. Praise; giving thanks; doing good; almsgiving; and communicating, or distributing, to others.

14. (a) Obedience and submission. (b) They watch over the souls of believers and must give an account for how they have discharged their duty.

15. (a) He asked them to pray for him and his associates. (b) His goal was to live honestly and have a clear conscience. (c) To be able to come and see them soon. (d) Patiently consider all he wrote to them since it was a long letter. (e) Timothy was free from prison, and they were both coming to visit soon.

16. (a) He is the great shepherd of the sheep, the One Who shed His blood and rose again from death. (b) Through Christ, God is making us spiritually mature and obedient so that we can bring glory to Him.

Section III—1. (a) Personality differences, background differences, diverse opinions, likes and dislikes, selfish desires (such as control), holding grudges, everyday stress. (b) Attitudes needed are humility, forbearance, and the ability to keep God's perspective.

2. Personal answers. (Ask your pastor for material on the persecuted church.)

3. Through reading material, television programs, movies, music, or computer sites that condone or expose us to sexual immorality. Even beyond this, why should any sexual act, even if portrayed as being within marriage, be part of our entertainment? Other sources are suggestive dressing and fantasizing.

4. By failing to ask God to meet our needs; by putting ourselves deeply in debt; by refusing to share with others. (*Discuss:* Is it wrong to have insurance or a retirement account? Do such things evidence a lack of faith? Why or why not?)

5. We should continually count our blessings. Don't compare what we have with others. Avoid sources that tend to make us think about getting more; e.g., catalogs, flyers, Web sites.

6. Personal answers.